MIND, BODY & SOUL IN BALANCE

BY JULIET MILLS

Published by:

The Publishing Mills
1680 N. Vine Street, Suite 1016
Los Angeles, California 90028

ISBN 1-879371-45-6

Cover Design by Sally Coates
Book Design by Dolphin Communications Inc., Washington, D.C.

CONTENTS

PRAYER

"The spirit is the life, the mind is the builder and the physical is the result".

- Edgar Cayce

Excerpts from CREATIVE VISUALIZATION by Shakti Gawain, copyright 1978 by Shakti Gawain, reprinted with permission of New World Library, San Rafael, CA 94903

FOREWORD

I have written many forewords to many books over the last forty years but this one, I felt, was going to prove very difficult.

The author happens to be my beloved daughter, our first-born, and I could see many pitfalls ahead because I have always been very critical of our children's work. But, having read this book, I now know I am going to find it difficult not to sound extremely biased. However, here is what I sincerely feel about MIND, BODY & SOUL IN BALANCE.

It is, first of all, written with a great sense of humour, amusing and sometimes outrageously funny. The author is a marvellous cook, I can personally speak for nearly all the recipes and, as she is a firm believer in the Hay diet, any reader who tries her concoctions need never worry about putting on weight.

The book, however, delves much deeper than that. It discusses healing, alternative medicine and reflexology and I can speak with experience of the latter. The author is a trained reflexologist and, six months ago, I suffered a crushed vertebrae. After several treatments from Juliet I had complete relief from the intense pain. Because she believes totally in healing it has become part of her, and that combination benefits the practical side of the treatment enormously. She is a great follower of Edgar Cayce and she brings many of his beliefs into the field of alternative medicine.

I can recommend this book as a thoroughly good read and I really believe it will give a great deal of pleasure.

Sir John Mills, CBE

INTRODUCTION

We are all on our own path toward understanding the meaning of life, and now it seems, more than ever, people want to share their discoveries and experiences, hoping it will help someone else along the way. I find almost everyone I know is interested in some form of Metaphysics, and in taking more control of their own lives, both in respect to their health and healing, and in developing their psychic potential and spiritual power.

Over the last 10 years I have gleaned information from many different sources; books, seminars, lectures and courses. I have practiced yoga and meditation, and attended psychic development classes; and I have experimented with my new-found, though ancient, knowledge, both on myself, and on my family and friends. It's all so simple, so logical and it works. The more one knows, the more one wants to know. We all want to improve the quality of our lives, and therefore the lives of those around us; if we are vibrating on a higher level of consciousness we lift those around us to a higher level also.

I have always liked helping people, making them feel better, cheering them up if they are sad or depressed, or nursing someone who is sick; there's nothing self-sacrificing about it, it's part of my nature. I found this out about myself as early as nine years old, when I was sent off to boarding school, which was a devastating experience for me. Up till then I had led a very sheltered, one could even say spoiled, existence, as the eldest child of rich and famous parents, who lived in a beautiful house with a nanny, a cook, a maid and a chauffeur. Suddenly I was hurled into this very spartan life (English boarding schools 40 years were very spartan) completely alone, knowing no-one, and removed from the security and support of my parents. I made a lot of discoveries very fast. One of them was that if I found a little girl who was very homesick and crying her heart out and I worked hard to cheer her up and make her laugh, I would feel better too! It was like magic. And so on the first ghastly night of a new term, which seemed to stretch endlessly ahead of us, if some poor little waif was sobbing into her pillow, the word would go round "to get Juliet". And after an hour of cavorting around the dormitory and telling stories, and hugging and stroking the one in despair, she would be smiling and feeling better, and so magically would Juliet, who also, if the truth be known had been sobbing into her pillow as well.

I even had to deal with a house mistress who despised me because I was "John Mills' daughter," which is what she referred to me as, rather than using my name! But it was all very character building and I learnt a lot of life's lessons early on, which have stood me in good stead. My best friend from those days, Jenny Wren, is still one of my best friends today.

I believe that anyone who is drawn to this book will find it helpful, in some way. And that is my reason for writing it.

As the health of the physical body relies heavily on the food we eat, I have also included some of my favourite recipes. I have loved cooking since I was a child, I still have the notebook that I used to write the recipes in for meals that Mummy's expert English cooks made for us. I love cooking for my family and friends, and since I've always been a working wife and mother, my recipes are for meals that don't take long to prepare, and that are both delicious and nutritious. Since I was brought up to believe "you are what you eat," the food I serve is definitely good for you, but that doesn't mean it's all brown rice and boring. I believe you can eat almost anything in moderation, as long as you don't eat it all at the same time, and that it is what you do eat, rather than what you don't eat that is important.

So get the body healthy and in balance, and get the mind calm and under control, and then you will be able to practice going deep inside to the source to the soul, deep inside yourself; and you will find a new sense of peace, and of power. There, inside your own being, are all the answers to everything, knowledge that can change your life and make your dreams come true. The health of all three, Mind, Body and Soul, and their balance and harmony with each other is the subject matter of this book.

Sir John and Lady Mary Mills

MIND
THE MIND AND MEDITATION

"The Mind is the builder ..."
"For as he thinketh in his heart - so is he"

- Edgar Cayœ
Proverbs 23:7

When you think about it, how often is your mind in the past or the future, rather than in the present moment? To be "in the moment" is one of the secrets to being happy; like a child, an innocent. If you are being in the now, the present, that means you are not worried or afraid of the future, and not sad or angry about the past. Worry, fear and anger cause stress, and stress causes disease and sickness.

The mind also limits us in certain ways, depending on how we have been conditioned, and through our own experiences. For example, I love to run, as a form of exercise, but also for the sheer exhilaration of my own strength and stamina. I can run 10 kilometres quite easily, and have done many times, but if I tell myself I'm going to have a 5 kilometre run along the beach, at the end of the 5 kilometres I'm tired, I feel I can't go on, I certainly don't feel I could run for another 5 kilometres. That is the power of the mind, it has limited me and my physical capacity.

If a woman who is pregnant has grown up hearing women talking of the 'terrible time poor so-and-so had in labour,' and how ghastly is the pain of childbirth, that woman is bound to have a more difficult time giving birth than someone who grew up in a gypsy caravan and heard her mother talk of squatting down under a bush and popping a baby out! Someone who has no preconceived ideas about it all, and who understands it is a natural phenomenon. The body is designed to push the baby out when it is time, and if the muscles are not hindered by the mind tensing them up, they will get on with it, and the pain is more than bearable. Natural childbirth classes teach you to breathe and relax; regulated rhythmic breathing stills the mind and relaxes the muscles.

I believe it is unethical and immoral for doctors to tell people who have terminal diseases how long they have to live - 3 months, 8 months, 2 years, whatever it is; you can be sure more often than not the patients prove their doctors right, because the mind is the builder. So how do we get this mind of ours a little more under control, and at the same time make it work for us, helping us to develop our unlimited potential? How do we also teach ourselves not to be so stressed out, and be more proficient at living in the now; how can we practice being in the moment?

Meditation is the answer. We all meditate at some time or another, maybe without realizing it. One often hears that women are more intuitive or more in touch with their feelings than men. I think this is partly because women have chores to do at home that promote unconscious meditation. Activities like sewing, knitting, ironing, baking, gardening, even vacuuming, where the mind is focused on something which allows the subconscious to surface, is a form of meditation, but because we are doing it unconsciously, more than likely we are not using it as a tool to improve our everyday life. I believe if you meditate regularly, you tend not to worry about things, because any question you have can be answered, any dilemma resolved, by you, yourself. When the body is quiet and the mind is stilled, the all-knowing self, the soul, can be tapped for the innate wisdom that most surely is there. The answer to everything is within ourselves.

Meditation is a very healing process; it brings health and well-being, stress reduction and clarity. And you start feeling the benefits immediately once you start practicing it. It brings the conscious part of oneself into a close attunement with the Divine within; the God Source within one's own being.

Edgar Cayce said: "Prayer is talking to God. Meditation is listening to God."

Now the question: How do I learn to meditate? It's so hard to shut the mind off, it chatters away constantly. Well, there are many ways, and there are some wonderful audio tapes one can buy which are very helpful to get you started, but, as in all things you want to become good at, practice is the key.

I have been meditating for about 8 years now, but I still have to set myself up for it. I like to burn incense and play soft music, and I make sure I will not be disturbed. I sit cross-legged on the floor and do some slow deep breathing exercises for about 5 minutes. One can also lie down or sit in a chair, but it is important your back is straight, and you shouldn't be uncomfortable because that defeats the purpose of the relaxation. Sitting in a straight-backed chair is nice because you can imagine the earth energy, the root energy coming up through your feet, as well as the cosmic energy shining down on your head. The breathing exercises can be as simple as inhaling for 4 counts, holding the breath for 4 counts and exhaling for 6 counts. Or inhaling for 5, exhaling for 10, then gradually increasing that until you are inhaling for 10, exhaling for 20.

After the breathing I repeat a mantra out loud or silently, internally. Mantra means "mind tool" and it satisfies our need for an unchanging mental stimulus of a highly creative and inspirational nature. It is one of the keys to harnessing the mind in the 'attunement' stage of meditation. Here are 3 mantras I use:

"I am a radiant being full of light and love."
"I am that I am."
"I am God in Light."
Or you can just chant "OM" which means God.

If intrusive thoughts keep bothering you, you can focus on an object or the flame of a candle; when our attention is fully engaged on one thought or one object, the mind eventually becomes silent, and the incessant internal chattering stops. So with the body completely relaxed, and the mind stilled, the spiritual energy moves upward through the chakras and you are able to tap into your Higher Consciousness.

The Chakras (literal translation "wheels of energy") are the seven spiritual or psychic centres in the body, and when you meditate the spiritual energy moves upward from the base of the spine, touching all seven of those centres, and there is a cleansing and balancing, a re-sensitising and a reawakening of those centres. It makes you feel calm and reassured, in touch with your self and your emotions.

Shirley MacLaine has released a wonderful videotape called "Inner Workout." In it she explains about the Chakras and takes you through two beautiful meditations. One is for cleansing and opening up the Chakras; and the other is a journey within to that peaceful place where you are in touch with your soul source. The Soul is the real self, the continuous self, it is all-knowing and very powerful. Even if you've never consciously meditated before you won't fail with Shirley, she makes it wonderfully easy.

Swami Vishnu Sivananda founder of the International Sivananda Yoga Centres formulated these 12 principles to help people understand the basic steps and stages of meditation. I've included them here because I found them very helpful when I was a beginner. I think it's particularly important to meditate at the same time each day to start with, so that the mind, the builder, becomes quickly programmed.

THE TWELVE PRINCIPLES

1. Set aside a special place for meditation; the atmosphere you build up will help still the mind.

2. Choose a time when your mind is free of everyday concerns; dawn and dusk are ideal.

3. Using the same time and place each day conditions the mind to slow down more quickly.

4. Sit with your back, neck and head in a straight line, facing North or East.

5. Instruct your mind to remain quiet for the duration of your meditation session.

6. Regulate your breathing; start with five minutes deep breathing, then slow it down.

7. Establish a rhythmic breathing pattern, inhaling then exhaling for about three seconds.

8. At first, let your mind wander; it will only grow more restless if you force it to concentrate.

9. Now bring the mind to rest on the focal point of your choice, a chosen mantra.

10. Applying your chosen technique, hold your object of concentration at this focal point throughout the session.

11. Meditation comes when you reach a state of pure thought, but still retain your awareness of duality.

12. After long practice, duality disappears and samadhi, the super-conscious state, is attained.

N.B. You can also meditate on the subway or on a bus!

"In the same way that focusing the rays of the sun with a magnifying glass makes them hot enough to burn, just so focusing the scattered rays of thought makes the mind penetrating and powerful."

Swami Vishnu Sivananda

There is no doubt about it, I get my best ideas, creative and otherwise when I'm meditating. One can direct one's meditation too, you don't just have to stay blank. If you have a problem, ask for guidance, and trust the response.

As a matter of fact, how I finally came to start writing this book was during a meditation. One night last year, although I was very tired for some reason I couldn't sleep; so after about 2 hours of tossing and turning, my mind going a mile a minute, I decided to get up and do a little meditation. I thought it would calm me down and make me sleepy, also I'd heard meditating in the wee small hours of the morning was a good time to do it, and I never had. It was 2 a.m.; it was very windy and I could hear the wind chimes outside the front door tinkling. I sat in the darkness of the living room, listening to the bells and doing my rhythmic breathing, when suddenly the first two sentences of the book came to me, they just popped into my mind. I was quite startled, I wasn't consciously thinking about the book at that moment, but I had been thinking about writing for weeks, and I just didn't know how to start, or what format the book should have. I quickly got a pad and pencil, and that night in the darkness, I not only got the first few pages written, but also I knew how I wanted to lay it out, the order of subjects, the beginning, the middle and the end. I scribbled away for hours hoping I would be able to decipher it all the next day. Now some people would call that 'automatic writing', and truly, sometimes I wonder where it's all coming from. But at the same time I know it's all there inside us, inside all of us, the knowledge, the wisdom, if we can only get to it. Meditation is a tool which helps us to do just that.

"Meditation is a continuous flow of perception of thought, like the flow of water in a river."

Swami Vishnu Sivananda

VISUALIZATION VERSUS
POSITIVE THINKING

Visualization is also a tool, a tool which can help you fulfil your dreams and direct your destiny. Some years ago a friend gave me a book called "Creative Visualization" written by Shakti Gawain. It is a really wonderful little workbook, and I have given it to many of my friends. Shakti's definition of visualization is simple:

"The technique of using your imagination to create what you want in your life."

In her book she teaches the art of using mental energy to transform and greatly improve your health, beauty, prosperity, love relationships and the fulfilment of your desires.

I have been consciously working with visualization for a few years now, it is indeed a fascinating study. As in all things that you want to be proficient in, practice makes perfect. You have to work continuously at improving the quality of your life. And if you do you are rewarded. But you have to strive, to make the effort on every level you can; practical effort as well. It's no good visualising something you want to happen, and then not making any effort on any other level.

For example, I remember once when my husband Maxwell and I had been visualising a lovely job coming along for him, because he'd had a few months out of work, an actor's occupational hazard I'm afraid, one morning he sat down with a list of every casting director he had ever met or who had seen his work, and he systematically called every single one of them, personally. It's not an easy thing to do, calling people and selling, not a commodity, but yourself, and I really admired him for it. And of course, out of it came a job - who's to say if it was the visualization or the hustling that brought the offer; he had done everything he could do, that's the point.

When you visualise something you want to happen, set the scene with your imagination; see it, smell it, taste it, feel it. If, for example, you are going on an interview for a job, see how confidently you walk through the door and sit down, see what you are wearing, see the positive effect you are having on the people in the room, experience the interview step by step, the way you want it to go. Then receive the letter or the phone call saying you've got the job. Feel the excitement and the pleasure, etc.

Positive thinking is altogether different from Creative Visualization, and it is not 100 per cent effective. It has some positive effect on you, but the conscious thinking mind is only one tenth of your total consciousness, and many times the positive thoughts you force on your mind push the negative thoughts deep inside. You think positive, but deep inside you believe there is a negative, and the more you try to force the positive thought, the negative thought goes deep down somewhere inside you. Negative thoughts come from stress and tension. Anger, violence and depression come from stress and tension, so what we have to do is eliminate negative thoughts, by going deep inside ourselves with breathing, with meditation, and finding the joy that is there waiting to be found.

"I am a radiant being, full of light and love."
Say that a hundred times and see how good you feel!

Affirmations are one of the most important elements of visualisation. To affirm means "to make firm." An affirmation is a strong statement that something is already so. It is a way of making firm that which you are imaging. They can be done silently, internally, spoken aloud, written down and of course chanted. Shakti uses affirmations like:

"The light within me is creating miracles in my life here and now."

and

"I am now perfectly attuned to my higher purpose and the divine plan of my life."

A new one I've been using recently is:

"Everything I really need is coming to me now."

Another good thing about visualization is it makes one be specific about what you want. How can a desire or a dream manifest if you haven't even thought it yet? It's no good just complaining, saying things like: "I wish things were different," or "I wish I didn't live here" or "I wish I had another job." Say exactly what you would like to be different, or where you would like to live, or what job you want. Specify, paint pictures, use your imagination. Put it out there in the Universe where it can draw energy, and thus materialize. Everything starts with an idea, everything you look at was an idea first.

When a friend calls me up depressed, or feeling insecure in some relationship or their job, or just feeling incomplete in some way my advice is do something about it, both on the practical level and on the soul level. Go to a beginner's yoga class one evening instead of watching TV, buy a tape that will help you meditate. Go and sit in the park or at the beach, watch the sunset and go deep inside yourself and observe the sensations. Visualize the turn you want your life to take, and because you have done something about your predicament and/or your state of mind, because you have made the effort, no matter how small, you will get the help you need.

"This wisdom may be heeded by every man who would improve himself and strive to realize the highest goal of life: God. What we consistently think about will influence what we become. Our circumstances in life, our moods and habits, our successes and failures, are largely products of our thoughts. Indeed the power of the mind is the originating and governing force behind all creation."

SRI DAYA MATA
President of the
Self Realization Fellowship

THE BODY:
HEALTH & DIET

"I shall recognize all disease as the result of my transgressions against health laws and I shall try to undo the evil by right eating, by less eating, by fasting, by more exercise, and by right thinking."

Obviously what we eat is of paramount importance to our physical health. What we eat feeds the tissue, the cells, the brain, the muscles, the bones and the blood. If we eat food that is refined and bleached, with all the nutrients taken out of it, like white flour and white sugar, and vegetables that have been cooked, literally to death; and we don't eat enough live fruit and vegetables bursting with the minerals and vitamins that our bodies need; and we eat too much meat which is very hard to digest and high in cholesterol, then eventually, inevitably, we will wear the body down, and we will get sick.

I was lucky to be brought up eating very healthily because my parents believed the old adage "you are what you eat." For most of my childhood we lived on a beautiful farm in Kent, the garden of England. We ate fresh salads and fruit and vegetables from the garden; fresh milk and butter and eggs from the farm; fish, chicken, roast meat on Sundays; and as much brown sugar, honey, and maple syrup as we liked, but no white sugar and no white flour. Daddy called them "robber foods," they take away from the system rather than nourish it.

My parents, Sir John and Lady Mary are truly a great testament to their way of life. He is 85 and proud of it, and she is getting up there, and mysterious about it; we've never known how old Mummy is but she must be over 80, and she really doesn't look her age. Her hair is still a beautiful red-gold; her eyes and her mind are bright. Daddy works, making films, learning lines, and making speeches; and travels all over the world to do it.

But if either of them do feel overtired or unwell they immediately go on a very strict diet, making sure everything they eat is what the body needs to heal and replenish itself. The particular diet they use and have used for years, ever since Daddy was invalided out of the army, is the Hay Diet. In 1940 he was diagnosed as having a duodenal ulcer and was really very ill, and unable to eat; his sister Annette implored him to go on this Hay Diet. The Hay Diet was introduced by Dr. William Howard Hay in the early 1900's. Dr. Hay was born in Pennsylvania, USA, in 1866. After

Sir John Mills, C.B.E. at 80 yrs old. The Proof of the Pudding

Lady Mary shining in her Seventies

gaining his medical degree at New York University in 1891 he practiced for sixteen years, until ill health made him doubt not only his training, but the whole system of conventional medical treatment and its application. He concluded that freedom from disease lay not in relieving symptoms, but in treating the underlying causes.

One hundred years later, this very same principle is being increasingly upheld by practitioners of our day supportive of what is now termed 'holistic', or 'complementary', medicine.

His personal research resulted in his discovery that a balanced diet, with foods eaten in a combination so as to avoid a mixture of starch and protein at any one meal, leads to the alleviation of numerous symptoms of disease, and offers renewed health. This then led him to establish two further principles of his system of eating; the necessity of balancing the alkali to acid ratio of the body and ensuring regular and efficient waste food elimination.

He went on to develop and define his principles of eating, establishing 'The Hay System' and his book Health via Food was published in 1934. Daddy has a copy and Mummy has written on the fly-leaf - 'John Mills Bible'. Adaptations of the Hay system can be found in the Beverly Hills Diet, The Wright Diet, and Fit For Life. It is not a new concept - it's an old concept. From the Essene Gospel of Peace, a third century manuscript, come the words:

'Cook not, neither mix all things one with another, lest your bowels become as steaming bogs ... For I tell you truly, if you mix together all sorts of food in your body, then the peace of your body will cease, and endless war will rage in you.'

This way of eating is in no sense boring, it's not a diet of self-denial - it's a delicious way to eat, and it's a stimulating challenge for the cook.

A typical Hay Day.

Breakfast
Fruit and yoghurt, fresh coffee and milk. No sugar.

or

Weak tea, wholewheat bread or toast and butter, honey if desired.
Oatmeal. No milk.

Lunch
Baked potato and salad.

Dinner
Any of the proteins: meat, chicken, fish, eggs, cheese,
and any vegetable except potatoes
and sweetcorn. No flour.

Or, have eggs and bacon for breakfast if that's the way you

like to eat - but no toast and no sugar. Have the fruit and cheese at lunch with salad, etc.

And if you want tea, no milk, you can have weak tea, and treacle tart - no cream, or sweet biscuits and cake. You see you can literally have your cake and eat it. And the theory is so logical - so entirely understandable - the body gets too acid acting and reacting - and we have to balance it with alkali-forming foods.

Chemically speaking food is either alkali-forming or acid-forming in its makeup, and for this reason has a direct influence on the overall alkalinity or acidity of the body.

Jackie Le Tissier has a wonderful food-combining vegetarian cookbook based on the Hay Diet, and to quote her-:

"There are Five Basic Rules to remember.

1. Starchy foods and sugars (carbohydrates) should not be eaten with proteins or acid fruits at the same meal

2. Fruit, vegetable and salad foods should form the major part of the diet

3. Starch foods and sugars (carbohydrates), proteins and fats should be eaten in small amounts only

4. Only wholegrain, unrefined carbohydrates should be eaten; all refined, processed foods - in particular white flour, white sugar and their by-products; highly processed fats; sweetened foods; foods containing unnaturally-occurring additives, preservatives and colourings - should be eliminated

5. There should be an interval of four to four-and-a-half hours between meals of different types"

Dr. Hay believed in juice fasting too (see following chapter) and the ideal way to embark on this diet is to first fast for 3 days and then start the new system. The object is to feed the body so that the alkaline balance is maintained and the blood is kept clean. This naturally prevents the accumulation of waste matter within the body.

Dr. Hay believed in "eating fundamentally" as he called it, eating "only such things as he believed were intended by nature as food for man, taking them in natural form, and in quantities no greater than seemed necessary for his present need." One of his golden rules was never to mix starch and protein at the same meal. He taught his patients that there were four main causes of the accumulation of acid in the digestion:- eating too much meat; over consumption of refined carbohydrates; e.g. white flour and white sugar; disregard for the laws of chemistry as these apply to the digestion of foods; and constipation.

My Father maintains this diet anytime he's not feeling 100 per cent or when he's priming up for a demanding role, because he knows he is at his optimum best when he eats this way.

Not mixing starch and protein is not easy! It means cutting out some of my favourite combinations, i.e. eggs and toast, fish and chips, roast chicken and roast potatoes (starch and protein); but it certainly makes you feel very well. And if you're overweight you will lose, and if you're underweight you will gain. It is an exceptionally good way to eat for diabetics or people who suffer from arthritis or asthma or eczema. It doesn't mean cutting out starch and sugar either, it means when you eat those things, you eat them on their own. Daddy has lovely big 'teas'; brown toast literally dripping with honey, and any cakes and cookies he can lay his hands on, and his weight is the same as it was in 1941 when he married my Mother. In fact on their wedding anniversary, he wears the same beautiful tweed jacket he courted her in 50 years ago. So you don't have to starve yourself, or deny yourself some occasional sweets, but when on the Hay Diet you never combine them with protein.

Speaking of diets, I once had to gain 35 lbs for a movie called "Avanti" which was filmed in Italy. It was directed by the great Billy Wilder and starred the brilliant Jack Lemmon and me, affectionately known in the film as "fat-ass"!

Pamela Piggott – Avanti

Off camera with Billy Wilder and Jack Lemmon

The first 20 lbs went on fairly easily but the last 15 were a real effort. I felt full all the time, like the day after Christmas, and still I had to eat! 35 lbs is a lot when you're 5'2" and weigh 107 lbs. I only had 10 weeks before we started shooting, and I had promised Mr. Wilder I would be a tub when I arrived in Rome. I ate huge pancake breakfasts, big lunches, enormous dinners, cream cakes at tea-time, and I drank thick chocolate milkshakes before I went to bed! But even with all that gorging when I flew to London, on my way to Rome, I was still 7 lbs under the required weight. So Daddy put me on a very high carbohydrate diet that he came up with; it was called "The Carlsberg Special Brew Diet". Basically it meant that my Father and Mother and I were drunk for 5 days because they were on the diet with me! We drank quantities of Carlsberg Lager morning, noon and night; very fattening! Anyway it worked, 5 days later I was on my way to Rome, 7 lbs heavier, looking like someone had blown me up with a bicycle pump, and feeling very hung over. Mr. Wilder met me at the airport and was delighted!

When the film was finished I started the Hay Diet, and I lost the first 20 lbs very fast, but the last 15 lbs seemed to be stuck in all the wrong places, so I went on a diet called "The Grapefruit Diet". It has the same premise as the Hay Diet only a little more stringent, because for 10 days you cut out starch and sugar altogether and you eat half a grapefruit, or drink unsweetened grapefruit juice, before or after every meal. I have given this diet to many of my friends and it really works wonderfully fast. If you stick to it faithfully, you are guaranteed to lose 8-10 lbs in 10 days. And it almost seems as if you are not on a diet at all because you can eat as much as you want of the food you're allowed.

I found it in Vogue Magazine years ago, as a diet used by models. You can eat meat, fish, fowl, cheese, vegetables, salads with oil dressings, avocados, lobster dripping with butter, eggs, bacon, ham, artichokes, oysters, snails, cauliflower, asparagus swimming in butter, in fact any vegetable (except obvious ones like potatoes, sweetcorn or baked beans) as long as you have your half grapefruit or grapefruit juice too. But no sugar and no flour.

It's an incredibly easy diet to be on secretly, one always appears to be eating like a horse and at the same time losing weight. You can eat half a chicken as long as you eat your half a grapefruit too! When I'm on this diet in preparation for work, and eating out, I carry one of those small cans of unsweetened grapefruit juice in my purse, in case the restaurant doesn't have any. Cut down on coffee though, it is thought to affect the insulin balance that hinders the burning process. Try to limit yourself to one cup per meal, and no diet sodas. The diet works best abstaining from alcohol of any kind but I believe an occasional glass of white wine is permissible. Experiment with your own metabolism, see if drinking wine slows down the slimming process. At least for the first few days stay teetotal, until you know how the diet affects you personally. It seems the grapefruit is the catalyst in this whole business. Catalyst, by dictionary definition is a "substance which facilitates a chemical reaction, but may or may not itself be affected by the reaction caused." The grapefruit somehow starts the fat burning process in the human body. And any diet which has a high protein content and low starch and sugar content is nutritionally proven. I put Maxwell on this diet a few years ago, in New York. He was doing a play with the divine Jessica Tandy; he was playing a young man who lived on the beach, no house, no money, no clothes! So he wanted to be a good 10 lbs under his normal weight, and the grapefruit diet did it for him. That's a good test for a diet, because when you're not fat, it's harder to lose weight than if you are. It's really quite a fun diet to be on, especially if you eat out a lot, and it really works fast which is so encouraging! I've never stayed on it longer than 10 days though, you get so sick of grapefruit!

"When the body and mind are in harmony, only then will there be an opportunity for proper spiritual development; for do not forget that the spiritual man is the first man, the mental man the second, and the physical the third man; and only when these second and third are in harmony can there be a proper spiritual state."

Dr. William Hay

FASTING

Fasting is an abstinence from food and drink for a period of time. A cleansing fast, for the purpose of physical detoxification and rejuvenation, is what I refer to here. It is a water, juice, and herb tea fast.

Fasting is a superb way to rest the internal organs, and the hard-working digestive system, and to rebalance the blood chemistry. Thus the body's great energy can be directed towards cleansing and purifying, healing and repairing. Fasting is the most ancient therapy known to man. Throughout the ages it has been seen as a means of spiritual growth in the practices of many religions. The American Indians fasted to see the great Spirit, and to obtain guidance and medicine power.

Maxwell and I fast for 24 hours on the first day of every month; it makes it easier to remember to do it that way. We do a carrot and orange juice fast that makes you feel light and bright and full of energy the next day. Abundant water and fruit and vegetable juices facilitate the elimination of toxins accumulated in the body from chemically treated food.

Be careful what you eat the day after the fast. As George Bernard Shaw said, "Any fool can go on a fast, but it takes a wise man to break it properly."

If you are at home carrying on normal activities, you should plan treats for yourself while you are fasting, like a massage or a sauna, or a soak in a hot tub with a mud pack on your face. Bathing and showering helps to get rid of toxins through the pores of the skin. And you shouldn't have to be around food or people eating. This starts the digestive juices running and you are instantly hungry. If, however, you are taking a lovely sunset walk on the beach, or in the park, or climbing a hill and giving yourself a little cardiovascular workout, more than likely you won't be hungry at all.

And if you are responsible for feeding your family, stock up your freezer so that on your fasting day you can take out a casserole or a lasagne, put it in the oven and leave them to it. I shut the door to my room and do yoga, or tidy my drawers.

Some of the other benefits from fasting:

- Heightened mental and spiritual clarity
- Mastery through self-restraint
- Elimination of drug cravings
- Elimination of sugar cravings
- Restful sleep
- Reduction of overweight if fast is followed with improved diet

Fasting is an excellent way to break any bad habit, any physical addiction, whether it is eating chocolate, drinking liquor, eating too much sugar (sugar is very addictive), drinking too much coffee or tea, smoking cigarettes or marijuana, or being dependent on some drug, prescription or otherwise.

Fasting stops patterns and eliminates cravings.

And one can fast anywhere one likes, one doesn't have to go to a health farm and pay money to be put on some diet. You can be in the privacy of your own home, under your own care and protection.

Unfortunately, our physical bodies become addicted all too easily and we get on "binges"; but whether it's a fudge binge or a beer binge, if we are in tune with ourselves, we can take care of ourselves much more easily than we are sometimes led to believe.

"Good and bad habits both take time to acquire force. Powerful bad habits can be displaced by opposite good habits if the latter are patiently cultured."

Paramahansa Yogananda

Truly after doing a 4 or 5 day fast, you will not feel like a cup of coffee or a glass of wine or a bag of M & M's; and if you don't have one, you won't want one till you do have one! But once you do relent, try to be moderate, moderation in regard to these physically addictive substances is the key. Have rules for yourself and stick to them.

Smoking is one of the hardest things to give up once you're hooked. I don't smoke cigarettes, I never had to give it up because I never seemed to have a good enough reason to start, mercifully.

Maxwell had to smoke in a play some years ago. He was not a smoker but the play, 'Journey's End', was about life in the trenches on the front line in World War II, and of course smoking was part of the fabric of life for the soldiers enduring that horror, one of the only pleasures of life. So Maxwell started smoking on the stage, and then off the stage and we were amazed at how quickly he became addicted; how quickly he was wanting that first cigarette of the day. He doesn't smoke now but we both occasionally smoke marijuana. I would personally advocate it over alcohol, if it were not illegal. Of course during the prohibition alcohol was illegal, so things can change around, the pendulum can swing.

I know if my daughter were at a teenage party and was going to be driven home by a boy who had smoked a joint or a boy who had a few pints of beer in him, which one I'd choose. The former's driving ability would not be impaired, and the latter would be a menace to himself and everyone else.

My Father doesn't like it because it is illegal, and I respect that. He doesn't object to the properties it contains, nor the 'high' it gives; he knows that having a smoke is ostensibly no worse than having a cocktail, but my Father is a true knight of the realm, and a law abiding citizen and it is an illegal substance. Unfortunately, I think.

It's a natural one though; it grows in the sun like the weed that it is. All the animals like it; rabbits, gophers, moles, and rats and mice will travel for miles to feast on a cannabis plant! Since time immemorial, down through the ages Man has looked to smoke herbs and eat mushrooms and to use substances that would "lift their spirit!" Native American Indians used peyote in a ceremonial way to be more in touch with the Great Spirit.

It is a shame that grass has been lumped in with narcotics as far as legality goes. It has no place with all the terrible manmade chemical drugs that are so destructive, it is a herb. If it were legalized, alcohol would not be the number one drug problem in the U.S., and road accidents would be down over 50 per cent!

Marijuana, or 'hemp' as it used to be known, has always been a valuable commodity on the international market. It is an Asian herbaceous plant, and in the days of the big sailing ships and outriggers, its fibre was used to make rope and stout fabrics. No doubt the sailors rolled up a few of the dry leaves and stuffed them into their pipes for 'Happy Hour' at sunset now and again!

I had my first smoke with Steve McQueen and his darling wife Neile in their bedroom in Brentwood, California about 20 years ago! I was about 30. I remember I kept insisting I didn't feel anything, and Steve said I had "lungs like an antelope!"

For my parents' generation it was alcohol, for my generation it was grass; I think my daughter Melissa's generation is more spiritually advanced than both of us, and realise they don't need anything to get them high other than a little chanting or a Hatha Yoga Session!

Obviously for the health of body and the spirit, chemical

drugs are ill-advised; this includes uppers and downers, sleeping pills etc. The new drug 'ecstasy' that seems to be the rage for the current youth of England is a very dangerous, chemically induced euphoria, which leaves people emotionally depleted and vulnerable, and eventually paranoid. And who wants a dose of paranoia, life is hard enough!

I am disciplined about my smoking and drinking. I don't do either when I'm working; or fasting; or if I'm on a special health programme of my own, because obviously it's best not to do anything - not smoke or drink, but the nature of our being is to enjoy the "fruits of the earth"; the fruits I say and not the poisons.

As far as your body goes, if you are smoking or drinking too much, you know it, you see and feel 'signs'; Stop - you are in control - go on a fast, interrupt the pattern, the habit, create a new regime for yourself, experiment. It is all a matter of choice - good health or bad. Go on the Hay Diet for a few weeks and see what happens. I'll tell you one thing for sure, you will feel better, and you will have more energy!

24 HOUR FAST

Upon rising have a small glass of warm water with a squeeze of lemon juice in it, or if you can't face that, a cup of herb tea with lemon and honey. At noon or lunch time sip a large glass of freshly squeezed orange juice and carrot juice. Visualise the vitamins and minerals nurturing your system. Sit down and relax for a few minutes and enjoy your lunch! At some point in the afternoon if you feel tired or hungry have another cup of tea; red zinger is one of my favourites, made with hibiscus flowers and very high in Vitamin C. I take it with a big spoonful of honey. And then at whatever time you normally have dinner, another large glass of carrot and orange juice - don't gulp it, sip it, and allow the body to assimilate the nutrients. It will satisfy your hunger. During this day of fasting, drink as much pure water as you can. Six 8 oz glasses would be good. It flushes the kidneys, cleanses the blood stream, and carries away impurities. Most people either forget to drink sufficient amounts of water or they underestimate just how much water they need for optimal health. This is probably the most basic dietary principle in Edgar Cayce's writings.

If you can treat yourself to a sauna or a steambath and a massage on this day, you should. Massage is an important therapy in any healing programme. Apart from it being a wonderful relaxing experience, a massage sends literally millions of impulses throughout the neurological pathways of the body and improves the circulation. If you can wangle a massage last thing at night, you sleep so deeply and you wake up from your 24 hour fast feeling wonderful.

4 DAY DETOX FAST

A couple of days before you embark on a four day fast prepare yourself mentally and physically. Get the fridge stocked up for the rest of the family, get the marketing done, and step up your fresh fruit and vegetable intake. Follow the same routine as for the 24 hour fast, carrot and orange juice, water and herb teas, with lemon and honey if you like. The first day is the hardest, it gets easier every day after that. Usually on the third day you experience the fasting "high"; you are full of energy and not hungry at all. Make sure you have at least 1 hour of exercise every day, preferably in the open air, walking is fine. Do some deep breathing and take warm baths and showers, because toxins are eliminated through the breath and through the pores. Saunas and steambaths are excellent for that reason. During this fast you are helping the body to rid itself of poisons accumulated in the system. Colonics by a licensed therapist or home enemas can be helpful for a total spring clean of the intestinal system. And keep warm, because while you are fasting your body temperature drops.

On the morning of the fifth day, don't eat until you are hungry, and then don't rush for the sugared cereal or the eggs and bacon; break your fast with fruit or a slice of wholewheat toast, then later have a salad or steamed vegetables. You will feel very pure and very pleased with yourself and you will have lost all of the bloat and some of the fat!

I do this fast 3 or 4 times a year.

EXERCISE AND YOGA

Exercise is a vital part of our programme for health and well-being. So many people have sedentary jobs; they get into the car, drive to work, sit all day, drive back from work, eat dinner and collapse in front of the TV. Edgar Cayce said walking was the best exercise of all. So, if like me, you are not into the aerobics groove, start walking, or running, or swimming or bicycling; but choose something you like, something you look forward to doing, that way you will be more likely to do it consistently. And try to do some form of exercise every day, even if it's only for half an hour.

I started running when I was 40. We were in New York City and Maxwell was enjoying a very successful season in Joe Orton's play, "Entertaining Mr Sloane" at the Cherry Lane Theatre. One day he persuaded me to run with him around a little track by the river. At first I couldn't run very far at all, but I gradually increased my distance, and a year later I ran in a 10 kilometre race in Beverly Hills. My time was 45 minutes and 38 seconds and I came 88th out of 1500 women of all ages. It was one of the proudest moments of my life! The family were so proud of me, and I was so proud of myself, and that of course is another secret to being happy, to feel proud of yourself, for whatever reason. Self esteem. I have grown to love running; I run on the beach or on a running track or on grass, but I don't like running on the road with traffic. It's harder on the body and the lungs, and no matter how young you are, never run without a good bra and proper shoes.

I run, I walk, I ride a bike occasionally and sometimes I swim, but yoga I try to do every day, or at least every other day!

HATHA YOGA

Hatha Yoga is more than just 'exercise,' more than just a way to tone up the muscles and strengthen the body, and massage the internal organs, though it does do all those things. It is scientifically designed to release the cosmic, psychic energy in the body. Just the same way the blood flow is blocked at certain stress points within the body, so the cosmic energy gets blocked. By constricting and releasing the flow at these points, there is a great "gush" as you release from the yoga posture, and the 'gush' carries the impurities and the stress and the tension away from that area. In the same way as you "kink a hose" to stop the water; when you release it, because the pressure has been building up, the water gushes out with extra force; so as you kink the body, stop the flow, then release it, the blood and the cosmic energy get a boost, the blood carries away impurities and toxins, and the cosmic energy flows powerfully through the system, cleansing and purifying and making it easier to get in touch with the elusive Higher Self.

Yoga is a Sanskrit word from the verbal root "Yuj" meaning: "To yoke or join, or fasten, or harness, as in horses to a chariot; to concentrate the mind in order to obtain union with the universal spirit. To be absorbed in meditation."

This is definitely another reason why I like yoga, apart from the feeling of well-being and centredness it gives me, it helps me get into that meditative state without almost any effort.

Yoga for me was, and is, one of the keys to attaining the quality of life to which I aspire. And the discipline of doing it regularly is a reward in itself. I started by going to a beginner's class a couple of times a week for a few months. Wherever you live you will probably be able to find a yoga centre in the yellow pages or the telephone directory. Now, I seldom go to a class, I do it at home, it has become a routine part of my life and I love it.

I put on some music (Kitaro is my favourite), and light some incense. I find it easier to focus if I set the scene for myself. I do a session of about 45 minutes to an hour, either in the morning, after my first cup of tea, but before I eat, or around 4 or 5 pm. Sunset is a lovely time to do it. It is good to do it at the same time every day; the body and mind become programmed very quickly.

In the following pages I describe the poses of a typical Hatha Yoga Session, and include sketches of the poses to go along with the instructions, it is much easier to follow this way.

A Yoga session with me begins with the "corpse pose" which is the classic relaxation pose. Lie on your back, feet spread about 18" apart and hands about 6" from your sides, symmetry provides proper space for all parts to relax. Close your eyes and breathe deeply, focusing your mind on your breathing. Relax for 2 or 3 minutes in this position. This is the pose you relax in after every "asana" (posture) until your breathing and heartbeat have returned to normal.

Next sit up, cross-legged, and do some head and neck exercises. Bend the head forward, trying to touch your chin to your breast bone, stretching out the muscles in the back of the neck, then bend the head backward as far as you can, then roll the head slowly clockwise, relaxing the tension.

Follow this with Sun Salutations. This is a series of 12 poses linked by a continuous flowing motion, and accompanied by deep breaths. (See illustrations). Yoga teachers say that if you only do one asana a day, it should be the Sun Salutation, it limbers up the whole body, and gets the blood flowing. It takes about 10 seconds, do 3 or 4, resting for a few seconds between each one.

Next there are the backward bending asanas; the Cobra, the Locust and the Bow. These poses are effective in strengthening the abdomen and lower back and legs; they massage the internal organs ensuring efficient functioning of the digestive system, combating menstrual irregularities and pain, and relieving constipation. They tone your back muscles and maintain the elasticity of your spine, improving posture and increasing vitality.

Hold each pose gently, breathing deeply and easily. I repeat a mantra internally; when you are uncomfortable come out of it and R E L A X into the corpse pose. There should be no pain in Yoga - just stiff muscles stretching out but no pain.

Next the forward bending asanas, which also invigorate the internal organs, reduce fat, and stimulate the entire nervous system.

Then comes the shoulder stand and its complimentary pose the Fish. The shoulder stand invigorates and rejuvenates the whole body. It is ideal as a pick-me-up, but most importantly it stimulates the thyroid and the parathyroid glands by pressing your chin into the base of your throat. The Half Spinal Twist awakens the spinal nerves and ligaments, massages the inner organs, and improves the digestion.

Last is the Headstand - the king of the asanas - and one of the most powerfully beneficial postures for both body and mind. It took me months to master this, I kept falling over!

According to Swami Sivananda, three asanas alone will keep your body in perfect health; the Headstand, the Shoulder Stand and the Forward Bend. If you cannot get yourself to a Yoga class to learn these postures, there are wonderful books and tapes you can buy with instructions that are very easy to follow.

The very first Yoga session you do in a beginner's class, or using a beginner's tape, or even following these simple instructions, you will feel the benefit, it is instantaneous. There is a certain amount of stiffness involved at the onset, but you do it at your own pace, and when you are hurting, you gently correct the posture and relax into the corpse pose. In a Hatha Yoga class the teacher never insists you hold a pose if you are in pain.

End the session with some breathing exercises and a short meditation. As I've said, as well as the physical benefits of these exercises, there is the amazing unblocking of the energy centres; the releasing of the bodily tension, which impedes the flow of spiritual energy, which is why after, even during, a Yoga session it is easy to meditate.

It is best to do Yoga on a fairly empty stomach, and if I'm not fasting I like to eat when I finish a session! So here are some of my favourite recipes!

SUN SALUTATIONS

1. Stand erect with feet together and palms in the prayer position in front of your chest. Exhale.

2. Inhaling, stretch your arms up and arch back from the waist, pushing the hips out, legs straight. Relax your neck.

3. Exhaling, fold forward and press your palms down, fingertips in line with toes - bend your knees if necessary.

4. Inhaling, bring the left, or right, leg back and place the knee on the floor. Arch back and look up, lifting your chin.

5. Retaining breath, bring the other leg back and support your weight on hands and toes, look at the floor between your hands.

6. Exhaling, lower your knees and then your chest and then your forehead, keeping your hips up and your toes curled under.

7. Inhaling, lower hips, point your toes and bend back. Keep legs together and shoulders down. Look up and back.

8. Exhaling, curl your toes under, raise your hips and pivot into an inverted V shape. Try to push your heels and head down and keep your shoulders back.

9. Inhaling, step forward and place the left (or right) foot between your hands. Rest the other knee on the floor and look up, as in position 4.

10. Exhaling, bring the other leg forward and bend down from the waist, keeping your palms as in position 3.

11. Inhaling, stretch your arms forward, then up and back over your head and bend back slowly from the waist, as in position 2.

12. Exhaling, gently come back to an upright position and bring your arms down by your sides.

THE COBRA

1. Lie down with your legs together and your hands palm down under your shoulders. Rest your forehead on the floor.

2. Inhaling, bring your head up, brushing first your nose, and then your chin against the floor. Now lift up your hands and use your back muscles to raise your chest as high as possible. Hold for a few deep breaths - then, exhaling slowly, return to position 1, keeping your chin up until last.

3. Inhaling, raise the trunk as before, but this time continue up and back until you can feel your back bending all the way down from the neck to the base of the spine. Breathe normally.

THE LOCUST

1. Lying on your front, inhale and roll onto your side. Make two fists and place them side by side, with thumbs pressing into your thighs. Bring your elbows as close together as possible.

2. Exhaling, roll over onto your front, so that you are lying on your arms, with your head resting on your chin. Take a few normal breaths in this position.

3. Inhale and raise your right leg, using your hands as a lever. Take two full breaths, exhale and bring the leg down. Repeat with the left leg. Keep both legs straight and don't swivel the hips. Then repeat with both legs raised.

THE BOW

1. Lie down on your front, head down and bend your knees up, then reach back with your hands and clasp hold of your ankles. Exhale.

2. Inhaling, raise your head and chest and, simultaneously, pull your ankles up, lifting the knees and thighs off the floor. Arch backward and look up. Take three deep breaths in this pose, then exhale and release it.

FORWARD BENDING - HEAD TO KNEE POSE

1. Sit up straight with your legs out in front of you, bend the right leg and bring the heel in, pressing the sole against your left thigh.

2. Exhale and fold forward from the base of your spine. Holding your foot in both hands, bring your head down your leg as far as possible. Breathe deeply, and release slowly. Roll down into the corpse pose and relax.

3. Repeat with the left leg bent, and both legs stretched out in front.

SHOULDER STAND

1. Lie down on the floor with your legs together and your hands by your sides, palms down. Inhaling, push down on your hands and raise your legs straight up above you.

2. Lift your hips off the floor and bring your legs up, over and beyond your head, at an angle of about 45 degrees.

3. Exhaling, bend your arms and support your body, holding as near the shoulders as possible, thumbs around the front of the body, fingers around the back. Push your back up, lift your legs.

4. Now straighten your spine and bring the legs up to a vertical position. Press your chin firmly into the base of your throat. Breathe slowly and deeply in the pose, gradually trying to work your elbows closer together, and your hands further down your back toward the shoulders, so as to straighten your torso. Keep your feet relaxed.

THE FISH

1. Lie down on your back with your legs straight and your feet together. Place your hands, palms down, underneath your thighs.

2. Pressing down on your elbows, inhale and arch your back, resting the very top of your head on the floor. Exhale. Breathe deeply while in the position keeping legs and lower torso relaxed. To come out of the pose, first lift your head and place it gently back down, then release the arms.

THE PLOUGH

1. Lying down on your back with your legs together and your hands palms down by your sides, inhale and raise your legs up. Exhale, then inhale, and bring your hips up off the floor.

2. Support your back with your hands, keeping your elbows as close to one another as possible. Then without bending your knees, exhale and bring your legs down behind your head. If you cannot yet touch the floor with your feet, remain breathing deeply in this position.

3. If your feet comfortably reach the floor, walk them as far behind your head as you can, and with your toes curled under, push your torso up and your heels back. Now clasp your hands together and stretch your arms out behind your back. Breathe slowly and deeply.

THE HALF-SPINAL TWIST

1. Kneel down with your legs together, resting on your heels. Then sit to the right of your feet.

2. Lift your left leg over your right, placing the foot against the outside of the right knee. Bring your right heels in close to your buttocks. Keep the spine erect.

3. Stretch your arms out to the sides at shoulder level and twist around to the left.

4. Now bring the right arm down on the outside of the left knee and hold the left foot in the right hand, placing your left hand on the floor behind you. Exhaling, twist as far as possible to the left. Look over the left shoulder.

THE HEADSTAND

1. Kneel down and rest your weight on your forearms. Wrap your hands round your elbows.

2. Release your hands and place them in front of you, with fingers interlocked. Your elbows now stay in this position.

3. Place the back of your head in your clasped hands and the top of your head on the floor. The hands and elbows form a tripod, making a firm foundation for the inverted body.

4. Now straighten your knees and raise your hips.

5. Without bending the knees, walk your feet in as close to your head as possible. Pull your hips back so that your neck is not bent backward or forward, but is in a straight line with the spine.

6. Bend your knees into your chest and lift your feet off the floor pulling your hips backward as you do so. Pause at this point, do not immediately attempt to raise your knees higher.

7. Then, keeping your knees bent, lift them up toward the ceiling, using your abdominal muscles.

8. Now slowly straighten your legs. You will feel most of the body's weight on the forearms. To come down, reverse steps 5, 6 and 7.

Rest in the Child's Pose for at least 6 deep breaths.

CHILD'S POSE

This relaxation pose is used to normalize the circulation after the headstand. Kneel down and sit back on your feet, heels pointing outward. Place your forehead on the floor, then bring your arms alongside your body, palms turned upward.

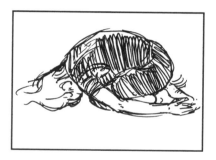

MEDITATION POSE

Sit in this pose, cross-legged with a straight spine for head and neck exercises, and for breathing and meditation. The hands should be resting lightly on the knees, palms up, with thumb and index finger touching.

RECIPES

The physical body is an amazing organism. Feed it and nourish it properly. It is almost invincible. Functioning at its optimum best, it will repair, regenerate, reproduce and replenish anew.

My first recipe is for Bread. It is a myth that breadmaking takes several days of hard labour, and it is almost impossible to find bread, real bread, in any supermarket. You certainly can't call those sickly white loaves that squash into nothing "the staff of life" of the Bible. Perhaps it is time to get back to the home baked loaf. The wonderful aroma of freshly baked bread that fills the house is almost a good enough reason on its own to get baking! This bread is so easy to make, even a culinary dunce can make it, and you can tell when you eat it that it benefits the system. If you had to live on bread and water alone, this bread would keep you motoring along a lot longer than any bread made with refined white flour, that's for sure. The amaranth flour I use is available at any health food store in the U.S., it is made from the amaranth root which was used by the Aztec Indians to improve the immunity system. That is why I use it in my bread, that and the fact that it gives the bread a delicious nutty flavour. To the ancient Greeks, the amaranth flower symbolised immortality. And the fantastic stamina of the Roman warrior was attributed to wholewheat bread and onions! I'll get to the onions later!

• • •

MY BREAD

Let your flour sit in the sun or on top of the warm oven; everything should be at blood temperature when making bread.

>6 cups stoneground whole wheat flour
>4 cups of Golds Wholewheat flour
>2 tsp. of salt
>*2 cups of amaranth flour
>3 tsp. dried yeast (3 pkts)
>2 tsp. honey or molasses
>5 cups of warm water (blood temperature)

Mix salt and flour. Put 3 tbsp. warm water in a cup. Sprinkle with yeast. Leave for 2 minutes. Add honey. Let stand for 15-20 minutes. When frothy, make well in centre of flour and pour in the yeast mixture and the rest of the warm water. Mix with warm hands until dough becomes elastic. Divide into 3 parts. Put into 3 warm loaf pans already greased, let sit, cover with a cloth on top of stove, or in warm kitchen for 20-30 minutes, till risen. Cook in hot oven @ 400 degrees for 35-40 minutes. When you knock on the crust and it sounds hollow your bread is baked.
*Amaranth flour can be found in most U.S. health food stores.

• • •

SALADS

If we have a staple diet in our house I suppose it would have to be "salad and baked potato". It certainly is one of my favourite meals, and the salad combinations are endless.

I always make the same dressing which everyone loves. I mix it on a dinner plate with a fork, a tip I learned in the restaurants of Italy. I use safflower oil because it is high in Vitamin E.

SAFFLOWER OIL DRESSING

1/3 cup safflower oil
1/2 tsp. red wine vinegar
1/2 tsp. Colman's mustard powder
1/2 tsp. of Marmite (optional)
1/2 tsp. salt
Pinch of sugar
Freshly ground black pepper

My Father adds chopped fresh garlic, lots of it! Garlic is one of the great natural antiseptics. He eats raw garlic and raw onions to get rid of a cold "instantly". He has been known to eat a raw onion like an apple on the film set, much to the chagrin of his current leading lady! I personally don't often put garlic in the dressing because it overpowers the more subtle tastes of some garden vegetables. But my Mother taught me to rub the wooden salad bowl with a raw clove of garlic, which gives the salad an aroma of garlic, but doesn't give anyone indigestion!

As I said garlic, and onions too, are great natural antiseptics; in World War I garlic was used as an antiseptic in hospitals, and researchers have found that in large amounts it can be effective as an antibiotic against bacteria, which may be resistant to other antibiotics. If people around you have colds or flu, hold a clove of raw garlic in your mouth, and you will be less likely to catch it. In Russia garlic is sometimes called "Russian Penicillin". Raw onions are good too; if any of my family seem to be coming down with a cold or a sinus problem, I make this onion salad for them. Believe me, it will clear your head very fast if you are bunged up with a cold! It burns it out! My kids always complained about it, but they ate it because they knew it worked.

• • •

ONION SALAD

1 Spanish or Maui onion, chopped coarsely
1 small can pitted black olives, chopped
1/4 lb cheddar cheese, cut in small cubes
2 cloves of garlic, chopped (optional)

Toss with safflower dressing and eat with celery stalks or brown bread and butter.

• • •

GARDEN SALAD

(so named because I grow all the ingredients in my garden)

1 head of lettuce (romaine or buttercrunch)
2 endives
1 bunch of arugula
6 medium sized beets boiled for about 45 minutes with skins on

Tear lettuce and arugula. Cool beets (the skins will slide off), slice or chop coarsely and add to greens. Toss with dressing. (This is a very good salad to have with a baked potato, the night before a fast.) Beets are very good for you, they are full of iron and calcium and iodine, and they purify the blood.

• • •

RED AND GREEN SALAD

1 head of lettuce
1 red and 1 green pepper
4 tomatoes
4 sticks of celery
1 avocado, sliced
10 slices of salami, cut into quarters

Chop and slice vegetables and toss into salad.

• • •

RANCH SPECIAL SALAD

Choose three different types of lettuce plus:
     arugula (optional)
     cooked beets
     cherry tomatoes
     chinese peapods or whole sugar snap peas
     avocado and jicama

Toss with dressing and decorate with sliced hard boiled eggs sprinkled with cayenne pepper. If you're feeling exotic, add a handful of raisins or walnuts or both.

• • •

SPINACH, EGG & BACON SALAD

Wash two bundles of fresh spinach twice, even thrice (because grit in the spinach can put you off for life). Tear into small pieces. Sprinkle with 8 pieces of crisp bacon crumbled. Add hard boiled eggs cut in half; if you add the bacon (drained on a paper towel) while it is still hot, it gives the spinach a nice wilted half-cooked flavour.

Serve with mushrooms fried in butter, adding a dash of sherry wine to the butter just before serving.

• • •

RED APPLE & WHITE CABBAGE SALAD

Finely shred a small white cabbage. Peel, core and dice four crisp red eating apples. Leave in a little peel for colour. Mix well with 1 dessert spoon of lemon juice. Blend 1/2 pint cultured cream with 1 tablespoon of mayonnaise. Add 2 teaspoons of mild mustard and a good sprinkling of celery salt. Blend with cabbage and apples and dust with paprika.

• • •

AVOCADO AND GRAPEFRUIT SALAD

Sections from 3 or 4 pink grapefruit
3 avocados, sliced
lettuce
Dressing:
2 cups safflower oil
1 cup cider vinegar
2 tsp. salt

1/2 cup of ketchup
6 tbsp. sugar
1 small onion grated
dash of pepper

In a blender combine oil and vinegar, ketchup, salt, sugar, onions and pepper. Set at high speed, blend thoroughly. Makes about 1 quart.

• • •

THE EUROPEAN CLASSIC SALAD NICOISE

1 clove garlic, split
crisp Romaine lettuce
4 small tomatoes
2 boiled potatoes
2 hard boiled eggs
1 cup drained cooked cut green beans
8-10 Italian-style black olives
8-10 anchovy fillets
minced parsley, paprika
onion rings
1 - 1 1/2 cups of flaked canned tuna
oil and vinegar dressing

Rub salad bowl or plate with garlic and line with lettuce. Peel tomatoes and cut into quarters. Peel and slice potatoes. Shell and slice eggs. Arrange tomatoes, potatoes, eggs, green beans and olives in piles on lettuce. Garnish with anchovies, parsley, paprika and onion rings. Heap tuna fish in the centre of the salad. Toss the dressing and serve immediately. Makes four to six servings.

• • •

WALDORF SALAD

Always a favourite - goes with everything.
Equal amounts of green apples, celery and walnuts, each chopped
and mixed with mayonnaise.

• • •

This is a great salad for a party. The bananas make it special.

MACARONI SALAD

2 cups large cooked spiral macaroni
4 hard boiled eggs
2 tbsp. spring onions, chopped finely
1 cup shredded cabbage
1 cup sliced celery
2 carrots, shredded
2 tomatoes, chopped
2 bananas sliced thinly
1 tsp. salt
1/2 tsp. white pepper
1/2 tsp. dry mustard

Mix together with 1/2 - 3/4 cup of mayonnaise. Add 2 oz
grated cheddar cheese. Sprinkle with sliced almonds.
Serve with a tossed green salad, and hot garlic bread.

• • •

VEGETABLES

We live on the coast of California, about 100 miles north of Los Angeles, and in this area one can grow almost anything. It is very similar to a Mediterranean climate, but without as much rain - unfortunately.

Gardening is one of my passions in life, inherited from my Mother and my English upbringing no doubt. As well as roses, I have over 150 rose bushes in the garden. I love to grow vegetables. There is something so wonderfully basic and satisfying about going out into the garden and picking the dinner! I grow lettuce, arugula, beets, carrots, cabbage, spinach, zucchini, eggplant, tomatoes, sweetcorn, beans, peas, swiss chard, cauliflower, collard greens, parsnip and onions; and herbs like basil, oregano, thyme, rosemary, mint and parsley.

We also have an avocado orchard and although we sell most of this wonderful fruit (it's called a fruit though one thinks of it as a vegetable) we eat a lot of it too, and I have experimented with it in the culinary sense, and I am amazed at its versatility. You will find avocado recipes popping up all through this section; it can be eaten hot or cold, in salads or soups, it is full of iron, has twice the potassium of a banana, absolutely no cholesterol, and is naturally rich in emollients and absorbent of ultraviolet light. It works with the body's elimination process, especially the liver, kidneys and lymphatic system; it is good for anaemia and building the body and is easily digested and absorbed into the system. The first dish I ever made with avocados was, of course, Guacamole. Naturally it is our favourite dip, and served with a variety of raw vegetables, or fresh tortilla chips, it is a delicious and nutritious snack or hors d'oeuvre.

GUACAMOLE I

Coarsely mash 4 avocados
Add 1 large, or 2 medium tomatoes, chopped
Add 4 spring onions, chopped (use green part as well)
Add salt to taste, a little paprika
and the juice of half a lemon
Presto!

A good tip: To keep the guacamole from going brown, leave one of the pits in it, until you are ready to serve it.

• • •

GUACAMOLE II

3 or 4 medium avocados mashed
1/3 cup red onions, chopped fine
1/4 cup cilantro, chopped fine
1 tsp. lemon juice
1 tsp. Worcestershire sauce
1 cup salsa (hot or medium - available in most markets)

Mix together, refrigerate for 2 hours.

• • •

AVOCADO ON THE HALF SHELL

2 perfect avocados, peeled, pitted and halved
4 pieces of bacon, cooked and crumbled
1/3 cup of ketchup
2 tsp. Worcestershire sauce

1 tbsp. lemon juice (fresh)
1 rounded tsp. brown sugar
dash of Tabasco sauce
1 tbsp. butter
1/4 tsp. Poupon mustard
freshly ground black pepper to taste

Combine bacon, ketchup, Worcestershire sauce, lemon juice, sugar, tabasco, butter and mustard. Cook over low heat until piping hot. Pour into halved avocados and serve on a bed of bibb lettuce along with tiny sprigs of parsley on top and a twist of fresh ground black pepper. Makes 4 servings

• • •

ZUCCHINI CASSEROLE

2 onions, thinly sliced
6 tbsp. butter
2 lbs zucchini, thinly sliced
2 med. sized tomatoes, thinly sliced
salt to taste
pepper to taste
1/4 cup grated parmesan cheese

Saute onions in butter until yellow. Add zucchini; cook and stir for 5 minutes. Add tomatoes, salt and pepper. Cover and cook until tender, approximately 25 minutes, or transfer to a casserole, sprinkle with grated cheese, and bake in 375 F oven until browned. Approximately half an hour. Serve with brown or basmati rice.

Leftovers make great filling for an omelette the next day!

• • •

CAULIFLOWER CHEESE AND CORN

1 cauliflower
1 can corn kernels or fresh corn, even better!
1/2 lb sharp cheddar cheese, grated
1/2 cup butter
3 tbsp. of flour
About 2 cups of milk
salt and white pepper

Boil or steam cauliflower, drain, place in casserole dish, cut in pieces or quarters. To make cheese sauce: melt butter in saucepan, add flour stirring constantly, remove from heat, add milk stirring until smooth, return to heat and add salt and pepper. Stir until thickened, add more milk if the sauce gets too thick, add the grated cheese, saving 1/4 cup to sprinkle on top. Stir until melted. Add drained corn. Stir until heated through then pour onto cauliflower in the casserole. Sprinkle top with remainder of the cheese and put under grill for 10 to 15 minutes or until top is brown and sizzling. A delicious supper dish. Serve with baked potatoes and butter.

• • •

This recipe for Almond-Zucchini Burritos won $500 in cash for Priscilla Yee of Concord, California, during the first Blue Diamond Almond Recipe Contest. The judges selected the vegetarian recipe because "it's a perfect complement to the nutritious almond". It's delicious and a favourite with our vegetarian friends.

ALMOND-ZUCCHINI BURRITOS

6 (8") flour tortillas
3 cups julienne zucchini, sliced 1" long

1/2 cup of onions, chopped
3/4 cup diced sweet red or green pepper
3 tbsp. oil
mild green chili salsa
2 tbsp. water
3/4 cup sliced natural almonds, toasted
3 tbsp. chopped cilantro or parsley
1 1/2 cups shredded cheddar cheese
1 cup of plain yogurt or sour cream

Wrap tortillas in foil and bake at 375 F for 10 to 15 minutes until heated through. Meanwhile, saute zucchini, onion and pepper in oil for 3 minutes or until tender-crisp. Reduce heat and add 1/3 cup salsa and water. Reserve 3 tbsp. of almonds for garnish. Stir in remaining almonds and cilantro. Spoon 1/2 cup of vegetable mixture down centre of each tortilla. Sprinkle with 1/4 cup of cheese. Roll up. Place on serving dish and spoon 1 tablespoon of salsa down the length of the burrito. Top with 1 tablespoon yogurt and reserved sliced almonds. Garnish with additional cilantro. Makes 6 servings.

"Those who would eat 2-3 almonds each day need never fear cancer...for the almond blossomed when everything else died."

Edgar Cayce

• • •

The next two recipes are taken from Sophia Loren's wonderful cookbook "Sophia Loren in the Kitchen with Love". Sophia taught me how to cook "Italian".

EGGPLANT PARMIGIANA

Clean and slice some large eggplants, say 2 lbs for 6 people. Each slice should be a little less than 1/4" thick. Place slices on a large plate, cover with coarse salt, then cover with another plate and weight it with something heavy so that the slices extrude their bitter juices. After a couple of hours, wash and dry the eggplant slices and squeeze them a little very gently to get them as dry as possible. Then fry them in plenty of bubbling olive oil. Make a sauce with tomatoes (say under 2 lbs or slightly less than the weight of eggplants), peel, chop them; put them in the pan with a pinch of salt and a few basil leaves, but without oil; you only have to wait for a little of the tomato juice to reduce before the sauce starts to thicken. At this point you put a few spoonfuls of the sauce into an oiled baking dish, then layer the fried eggplant and sprinkle with grated Parmesan cheese, then put down a layer of thinly sliced mozzarella with a few leaves of basil, and a spoonful of beaten egg. Begin all over again with the sauce, the eggplant, the cheese, egg, and back to home base, so that you end up with at least three layers of everything. Bake uncovered in a hot oven for 40 to 50 minutes.

Variations on this dish, which is revered through the length and breadth of Italy, include one with the eggplant dipped in egg and flour before frying; so that the taste is more delicate. It can also be made with half eggplant and half zucchini, which is still more delicate.

• • •

SOPHIA'S RATATOUILLE

Take 1 lb of eggplant, wash and dice. Put in a bowl with a good sprinkling of salt to absorb the bitter juice. This should be done at least three or four hours before you are ready to start cooking. At the right moment, brown a couple of very finely sliced onions in olive oil; then add 2 peeled and seeded tomatoes, 1 lb of zucchini, a couple of pimentos, seeded and cut into strips, optional; then the eggplant, after first washing away the salt and drying carefully; a minced clove of garlic (two if you like garlic); a small bunch of herbs (basil, parsley, marjoram, sage leaves); salt and pepper. Let cook for at least 1/2 hour until the ratatouille is a good consistency but not too dry.

• • •

MY BARBECUE BEANS

1 lb small pink beans (pinquinto)
4 slices bacon diced (optional - you can
substitute with 3 tbsp. of olive oil)
1 clove of garlic, minced
1/4 cup of red chili sauce (preferably Los Palmas brand)
3/4 cup of tomato puree
1/2 cup of dark brown sugar
1 tsp. dry mustard
1 tsp. salt

Pick over beans to remove dirt or small stones. Cover with water and let soak overnight. Drain, cover with fresh water and simmer for 2 hours or until tender. Saute bacon until lightly browned. Add garlic and saute 1 or 2 minutes longer, then add tomato puree, chili sauce, sugar, mustard and salt. Drain most of the liquid off the beans and stir in sauce. Keep hot over low heat until ready to serve. Makes 12 servings and keeps for days in the refrigerator.

• • •

My sister Hayley and I are old friends and we have always enjoyed cooking together. This is one of her recipes, she is a strict vegetarian; no meat, fish, chicken, not even eggs, so she has to use her imagination and expertise in the kitchen to make sure her family gets enough iron and vitamins. Lentils are high in both iron and calcium and the B vitamins.

HAYLEY'S LENTIL ROAST

1/2 lb continental (brown) lentils
2 cups wholemeal breadcrumbs
1 cup of sliced mushrooms
1 onion chopped
2 cloves of garlic, minced
2 cups of grated cheese, cheddar or Monterey Jack
1/2 cup of butter
mixed herbs
parsley
Worcestershire sauce

Cook lentils in salted water until almost done, but so the lentils are still firm. Gently fry onions and garlic in butter, add mixed herbs, salt and pepper and mushrooms and finally fold in breadcrumbs. Add drained lentils to onion mixture and add 1 1/2 cups of the grated cheese. Mix carefully. Put mixture in loaf tin or make into loaf and put in baking pan, and cover with the rest of the cheese. Cook in a moderate oven for approximately 3/4 hour, depending on how moist the lentils were. The top should be crisp and golden brown.

Serve with roast potatoes, roast parsnips, and green vegetables or salad.

• • •

ROAST POTATOES & ROAST PARSNIPS

First peel the potatoes, cut them in half and boil them in salted water until they are soft enough to get a fork into them; drain. Then add them to the chicken in the roasting pan (see recipe for Roast Chicken on page 87), rolling them around in the melted fat, and roast them for at least an hour and a half, turning them once, and basting them once more at that point. They will be crisp on the outside and soft on the inside. For vegetarians, use vegetable oil and a teaspoon of marmite (optional) in a baking pan, and after parboiling them, roast them in the oven for one and a half hours - turning once.

Parsnips can be done in the same way as the potatoes.

• • •

This is a wonderful quiche, avocados again! I often serve it to friends for lunch accompanied by a tossed green salad.

AVOCADO QUICHE

Pastry:
> 1 1/2 cups of flour
> 1/2 tsp. salt
> 1/2 cup shortening
> 1 egg, beaten
> 1 tbsp. spicy mustard
> 1/2 tsp. vinegar

In a 1 1/2 quart mixing bowl cut shortening into flour and

salt. Beat egg until foamy. Add enough cold water to equal 1/4 cup, if necessary. Mix mustard and vinegar with egg. Add to flour. Stir until mixture leaves sides of bowl. Form into ball and allow to rest for 5 minutes. Roll dough on floured board to fit a deep 9 inch pastry dish. Chill while preparing filling.

Filling:
2 California avocados
1 6 oz jar marinated artichoke hearts
2 cups (8 oz) grated cheddar or Swiss cheese
1 12 oz can evaporated milk
5 eggs, beaten
1/2 cup chopped onion
1/4 tsp. black pepper
1 tbsp. vegetable oil

Preheat oven to 375 F. In a small frying pan saute onions in the vegetable oil. Remove from heat. In a 2 quart mixing bowl beat eggs until foamy. Add milk and seasonings. Coarsely chop the artichoke hearts. Do not discard liquid. Peel and slice the California avocados. Add avocados, artichokes and artichoke juice, grated cheese and onions to the egg mixture. Gently blend. Pour into the chilled pastry shell. Place on lower rack in oven. Bake at 375 F for 45 minutes or until a table knife inserted in the centre comes out clean. The avocados will not darken when the quiche is baked or when any left-overs are refrigerated. The avocados will also rise to the top when baking and make a very attractive topping to the quiche.

• • •

VEGETARIAN CASSEROLE

1/2 lb butter beans, soaked overnight
1 lb leeks

1 large tin Italian tomatoes
potatoes
fresh Parmesan cheese
salt and white pepper to taste

Stir fry chopped leeks in butter. Add tomatoes and drained butter beans. Put in casserole. Sprinkle on some fresh Parmesan cheese, then spread mashed potatoes on top, and bake in a hot oven for about half an hour.

Serve with salad or cooked greens.

• • •

GOLDEN SWEETCORN AND POTATO CASSEROLE

2 tbsp. olive or sunflower oil
1 and 2/3 cups onion - cut in semi circles
1 vegetable stock cube
2 tsp. tumeric
1 and 1/4 lbs potato - peel and cut into small dice
2 cups sweetcorn kernels
1 1/2 tbsp. shoyu
5 cups boiling water
salt and freshly ground black pepper

Heat the oil, and fry the onion until soft. Mix in the stock cube and tumeric, and cook a further minute. Add the potato, sweetcorn and shoyu, then stir in the boiling water. Cover, bring to the boil, then simmer for 10-15 minutes or until the potato is tender, and season.

Serve with mushrooms, spring greens/collards and a mixed salad.

• • •

PASTA

I love everything about Italy, the food, the people, the art, the history and the way of life. In Italy fast food is not big business, Italians do not believe in eating their meals on the run, grabbing a hamburger or a hot dog and eating it in the car or walking along the street.

In fact, in Italy everything closes down between 1:30 and 4:00 pm for lunch! Digesting food is one of the body's biggest challenges, it takes a lot of energy, and it is not fair of us to expect it to do it efficiently while on the run; it is not surprising so many people complain of indigestion and heartburn.

Pasta, when combined with the right foods is easily digestible, not fattening, and quick and easy to prepare. Maxwell and I always eat pasta the night before a running race to stoke up on the carbohydrates.

SPAGHETTI AND TOMATO SAUCE

Serves 4
This has become a favourite in our family, and it is so easy to make.

> 1 lb spaghetti
> 1/4 cup of olive oil
> 8 cloves of garlic, peeled and crushed
> 2 large cans of peeled tomatoes or 7 cups
> fresh tomatoes, peeled and chopped
> 1 tsp. sugar
> a good pinch of salt
> a few fresh basil leaves (or 1 tsp. dried)
> Parmesan cheese

Heat oil with crushed garlic cloves till oil is smoking and garlic brown, remove garlic with slotted spoon, add tomatoes. Add sugar, salt and chopped basil. Stir and lower heat, simmer for 1/2 hour stirring occasionally. When spaghetti is cooked and waiting in a big serving dish, pour the sauce over the top and sprinkle with Parmesan.

• • •

MY LINGUINI WITH ASPARAGUS

Serves 4 to 6
> 1 1/2 lbs asparagus, cut on the diagonal in 1/2" pieces
> 1/2 cup olive oil
> 2 tsp. finely chopped garlic
> 2 lbs tomatoes, peeled and chopped coarsely (1/2 cup)
> 1 bunch scallions, trimmed and cut on the diagonal in
>   1/4" pieces
> 1/4 tsp. pepper flake
> salt and fresh ground pepper to taste
> 1 lb linguini
> 1 cup coarsely chopped basil
> Parmesan cheese

Put asparagus in a pot of cold salted water and bring to a boil and drain. Set aside. Heat olive oil in large skillet. Add garlic, tomatoes, scallions, pepper flakes, salt and pepper. Cook for about 4 minutes stirring occasionally. Add asparagus and cook for 1 minute to warm. Meanwhile cook linguini in boiling salted water to al dente. Serve immediately with grated cheese.

• • •

RED PEPPER PASTA SAUCE

Roast 2 red bell peppers over an open gas flame, under a broiler or in a hot oven until the skin is blackened. Remove skin under cold running water, remove seeds, core and slice into short strips; set aside. Add 1 cup fresh peas to saucepan of boiling salted water. Bring back to boil, remove from heat, cover and let stand for 5-8 minutes. Drain and set aside. Melt 2 tbsp. unsalted butter in a saucepan, add 2-3 finely sliced green onions, 1/2 cup diced cooked ham, a cup heavy cream and the peppers, let boil for 1-2 minutes. Stir in the peas, 1/2 cup grated Parmesan cheese, salt and pepper and freshly grated nutmeg. Combine with freshly cooked fettucine. Serves 4 people.

• • •

A great one to make when cherry tomatoes are in season.

FETTUCINE FERRARI

Serves 4

    1 lb Fettucine
    1/2 cup butter
    1 bunch green onions, chopped
    1-2 cloves garlic, minced
    1 cup cherry tomatoes, halved.
    4 oz ham, cut in 1/4" cubes
    1 egg yolk
    1/4 cup heavy cream
    1/2 cup fresh grated Parmesan cheese
    salt to taste
    freshly ground pepper to taste

In a large kettle, cook the fettucine in boiling salted water until it has reached the al dente stage, still firm to the bite. Drain thoroughly.

Melt the butter in a medium skillet. Add the scallions and garlic, cooking gently until the onions are tender. Add the tomatoes and saute for 1 to 2 minutes. Add ham and heat through. Beat the egg yolk and then beat the cream into the egg until well mixed. Slowly stir into the tomato and ham mixture with a flat whisk and cook until thickened and well blended. Add the sauce to the hot fettucine, toss and serve immediately on warm plates.

• • •

This is another of Hayley's recipes and a perfect dish to make if you are having guests because the sauce can be made ahead of time. It's very much a summer dish because the basil must be fresh and plentiful.

HAYLEY'S TOMATO AND BRIE TAGLIATELLE

4 ripe large tomatoes, cut in cubes
1 cup fresh basil, cut in strips
3 garlic cloves, minced
1 cup + 1 tbsp. olive oil
2 1/2 tsp. pepper
1 1/2 lbs tagliatelle or linguini
1 lb brie cheese, cut in irregular pieces with the rind off

Combine everything (except pasta, 1 tbsp. of oil and Parmesan) at least 2 1/2 hours ahead. It can be combined in the morning. At meal time cook pasta in water with 1 tbsp. olive oil, drain pasta and mix well with the tomato brie elixir; (the brie should melt). Sprinkle with Parmesan and serve.

• • •

LASAGNE

Sauce:
>1/2 cup olive oil or salad oil
>2 medium sized onions, chopped
>4 cloves of garlic, minced
>3 cans tomatoes or 7 cups fresh tomatoes, skinned and chopped
>2 6-oz cans of tomato paste
>1/2 cup of water
>1 cup chopped celery
>1 cup sliced mushrooms
>1/4 cup chopped parsley or flakes
>2 tbsp. sugar
>1/4 tsp. pepper
>2 bay leaves
>1 tsp. dried basil or 2 tsp. fresh basil

Heat oil in large kettle. Add onions and garlic, saute for 5 minutes. Stir in remaining ingredients. Bring mixture to a boil, reduce heat and simmer for 3 hours, stirring occasionally. Remove bay leaves and let cool.

>1 lb lasagna noodles
>1 tbsp. olive oil
>5 cups of sauce
>2 cups (1 lb) cottage cheese or ricotta cheese
>2 8-oz packages Mozzarella cheese, thinly sliced
>1/2 cup Romano or Parmesan cheese, grated

Lightly oil baking dish (13" x 9" x 2" or smaller and deeper dish). Boil noodles stirring frequently to prevent sticking for about 15 minutes or until almost tender. Drain and cover with cold water. Line bottom of dish with single layer of noodles, spoon over 1/4 of sauce and cottage or ricotta cheese, top with 1/4 of

Mozzarella and Parmesan cheese, repeat to make 4 layers ending with cheese on top. Bake at 350 F for 30 minutes.

Serves 8 very generously.

• • •

SPAGHETTI WITH OIL, GARLIC & BROCCOLI

3/4 cup olive oil
6 cloves garlic, chopped
3 tsp. anchovy paste (made by pounding anchovy
fillets in a mortar with a few drops of olive oil)
freshly ground black pepper
handful of chopped parsley
2 cups fresh broccoli, florets - steamed
1 lb spaghetti

Combine oil, garlic, anchovy paste and pepper with parsley in saucepan. Let it cook for a few minutes; the sauce is ready when it starts to acquire a golden tone without becoming too dark. At this point, turn the spaghetti which is now on the verge of being al dente into the pan and let it cook for a few minutes more, stirring easily so that the sauce is perfectly distributed. Add the broccoli, pour into large bowl, season with Parmesan or pecorino cheese.

• • •

LINGUINI WITH WHITE CLAM SAUCE

1/4 cup butter or margarine
1 tbsp. grated onion
1 clove garlic, minced
2 tbsp. flour
2 (10 1/2 oz) cans minced clams

1/4 cup dry white wine
1/3 cup chopped parsley
1/2 tsp. marjoram
1/2 tsp. salt
1/4 tsp. hot pepper sauce
1 lb linguini

Melt butter, add onion and garlic and cook over medium heat for 3 minutes. Sprinkle with flour and blend well. Add liquid drained from clams, wine, parsley, marjoram, salt and hot pepper sauce. Simmer uncovered for 10 minutes. Stir in clams and heat. Cook linguini according to package directions and drain. Serve clam sauce over hot linguini. Makes 4 servings.

• • •

When Maxwell and I were last in Rome, we were entertained by the incomparable master of design and elegance, Valentino. His beautiful villa on the Appian Way is exquisitely romantic, full of rich colours and textures; fresh flowers everywhere filling the house with perfume; great elegance as well as supreme comfort. We ate delicious food and drank delicious wine. I asked Valentine to give me a favourite recipe of his for my book. He gave me two. I wrote them down as he told me.

VALENTINO'S SPAGHETTI AL PESTO

4 cups of basil
a little parsley
handful of pinenuts
1 glass (cup) of olive oil
1 tbsp. of butter
1 cup each of Pecorino and Parmesan cheese
salt and pepper

Blend in a blender basil, parsley, pinenuts, butter, olive oil, salt and pepper and cheeses. Boil spaghetti, add some boiled potatoes and green beans, toss all together with pesto.

• • •

Juliet with Valentino

RISOTTO ALLA ROMANA

A cup or two of warm boullion or chicken stock
1/2 cup of olive oil
1/2 cup of butter
1 large onion, chopped
saffron
salt
1/2 cup of cream

Parmesan cheese
2 cups of rice (1 handful of rice per person)

In a skillet heat olive oil and butter. Saute chopped onion until golden, remove onion leaving olive oil and butter. Add rice, stirring with a wooden spoon. When rice becomes golden, add ladles of boullion gradually, stirring all the time. (Rice cooks for about 20 minutes). Add saffron and salt to taste. When ready add 1/2 cup of cream and sprinkle Parmesan on top.

Valentino says he sometimes serves this with a salad of Mache lettuce, arugula, sliced (fresh) parmesan and black truffles, tossed with an oil and vinegar dressing. Delicious! Viva Italia!

• • •

Not really Italian pasta...this is English pasta.

MACARONI CHEESE SUPPER DISH

1 lb macaroni
1/2 lb grated cheddar cheese
4 medium tomatoes
1/4 lb ham (optional)
2 tsp. flour
6 tbsp. butter
2 cups milk
1 tsp. salt
1/4 tsp. white pepper

Cook macaroni in boiling salted water, drain and put in warm pyrex or casserole dish, add tomatoes (skin them by letting them sit in boiling water for 5 minutes) and 4 rolled slices of ham. Add cooked macaroni and make cheese sauce (same sauce as for cauliflower cheese). Melt the butter in a saucepan, make roux by adding flour, milk and seasoning. Add grated cheese (save about 2 tablespoons of cheese to sprinkle on top). Pour sauce over the macaroni in the casserole and sprinkle with remaining cheese and put under the broiler for approximately 10 minutes until brown and bubbling. Serve with a tossed green salad.

MEAT

"Destiny or Karma depends on what the Soul has done about what it has become aware of."

Edgar Cayce

I was brought up in a traditionally English family, and one of the traditions I loved was Sunday Lunch. It was the meal everyone in the family looked forward to, not only for the food that was served but for the guest list. Mummy and Daddy would invite their exciting and glamorous friends to Sunday Lunch at the farm. I can remember sitting down at the table with people like Noel Coward, Lawrence Olivier, Vivien Leigh, Rex Harrison, Kay Kendall, Montgomery Clift, Tyrone Power, etc. How I wish that I had been taking notes or manning a video camera. They certainly were a glamorous group, full of gaiety and talent.

Sunday Lunch in England is traditionally roast beef or roast lamb, roast potatoes and fresh vegetables, followed by a pudding or dessert. The aroma of the roasting meat would have you in a state of mouth-watering anticipation by the time you sat down to eat. I still love the smell of meat cooking, roasting or barbecuing, and I still like the taste of it, and truly believe eating meat occasionally is good for you, it feeds the muscle and the bone. But gradually over the last few years I have cut down, and now have more or less stopped eating red meat altogether. Times have changed, the world has changed, and meat is not the same as it was years ago. The animals are not grazing out on the open prairie where they belong, living out what life they have in a natural environment; they are mass-produced in the most horrific conditions, they are injected with chemicals and antibiotics to make them fat and tender, which are then ingested by us second-hand, and they are slaughtered in cruel and inhumane ways.

Once one is really aware of all this, it changes your feelings about that Sunday roast or that steak or hamburger or hotdog. It is quite a dilemma, it is not easy to change the eating habits of centuries, but we can and should at least cut down on the amount of meat we eat. It is not good for one to eat too much meat anyway, it puts a heavy burden on the digestive system, and is the main cause of heart disease, high blood pressure and colon cancer in the U.S. today.

Meat takes a lot of moving along the tract, let's put it that way. We have an intestinal tract like a rabbit, not a cat, very long; carnivores have very short intestinal tracts. And festering flesh certainly gives off worse gases and toxins than festering fruits and vegetables, so it is logical to assume if you are a heavy meat eater (steaks and hamburgers) it is all the more important to step up the roughage, the bran and the fresh fruits and vegetables. This helps to keep the body healthy, assimilating and eliminating as opposed to getting bogged down, or clogged up, whichever way you like to put it.

Unfortunately whether meat is good for you is no longer the only issue, there are the moral and ecological ramifications involved. It really seems that one can no longer consider oneself humane if one eats meat in America or the U.K. anymore. Although the meat producers try to keep the gory details hidden from the public, they are leaking out, and they are shockingly horrifying.

Each day in the United States nine million cows, calves, pigs, chickens, and turkeys meet their death at human hands! That is ludicrous, monstrous.

I wonder how many of us would become vegetarian if we were asked to spend a day visiting a slaughterhouse or a factory farm. And it's not just the cruel and ghastly way that animals die, it is the torturous lives they live as well. We cannot go on saying, "Don't tell me what happens to the animals, it will spoil my dinner". We have to take responsibility, each and every one of us.

Further evidence for a vegetarian Hay System comes from the Essene Gospel for Peace written in the 3rd century. This states:

> "Kill neither men, nor beasts, nor yet the food which goes into your mouth. For if you eat living food, the same will quicken you, but if you kill your food, the dead food will kill you also ... For everything which kills your foods, kills your bodies also ... And your bodies become what your foods are ..."

Strangely prophetic in these days of concern about additives and second-hand drugs that we absorb into our system.

And then there is the vital issue of world hunger and deforestation. It's all connected. You may not give a thought to the rainforests as you waltz into McDonalds for your third hamburger of the week, but once you do, then you have to do something about it.

John Robbins' book, "Diet for a New America" is an astounding volume of research on this subject. The facts and figures are mind boggling; most of us have no idea what this excessive, unnecessary, unhealthy consumption of meat in this country and in the U.K., but in the U.S. particularly, is doing to the rest of the world.

> "Lester Brown of the Overseas Development Council has estimated that if Americans were to reduce their meat consumption by only 10% it would free over 12 million tons of grain annually for human consumption. That, all by itself, would be enough to adequately feed every one of the 60 million human beings who will starve to death on the planet this year."
>
> Diet for a New America

The amount of grain it takes to feed 100 cattle would feed 2000 people. An acre of land will produce 20,000 pounds of potatoes; that same acre of land will produce only 165 pounds of beef.

It is obvious which provides more food for a starving world.

Deforestation continues all over the world to make land for meat production. Now the rainforests in South America are being ravaged, as Mr Robbins so eloquently puts it:

"These jewels of nature are being rapidly destroyed to provide land on which cattle can be grazed for the American fast food market".

A shocking statement indeed - an indictment of our society. All of these reasons are why our family no longer eats beef; not veal either, a veal calf's story, according to Mr Robbins' research is not a pretty one.

It's hard to wean yourself from something you've always enjoyed, something you've been told is good for you. But that was then and this is now, and in the last years things have gone very wrong, and we cannot ignore them any longer. This is why there are no meat recipes in this section. Read on for chicken and fish!

• • •

ROSA'S FAMOUS CHICKEN SOUP

Rosa, a Nicaraguan, was my housekeeper for almost 17 years, she looked after both my children, Sean and Melissa, and she taught me to make this delicious and nutritious soup. If I am working I make this at the weekend and we all live off it for days. Second and third day it tastes even better. Children love it, and if you are not feeling well, it will make you feel better.

1 whole chicken, cut up
2 onions, chopped coarsely
2 tomatoes, chopped coarsely
1 tbsp. vinegar
2 tsp. salt
1 tsp. pepper
1/2 cup ketchup

4 or 5 sprigs of fresh mint
4 stalks of celery
4 large carrots
2 sweet potatoes, peeled and sliced thickly
(ordinary potatoes will do)
4 zucchini
1/2 head of cabbage (optional)
1/4 lb angel hair vermicelli

Put cut-up chicken in a big saucepan, cover with cold water, add onions, tomatoes, vinegar, ketchup, salt and pepper and mint. Bring to boil, then simmer for an hour or until chicken is tender. Add vegetables, except zucchini and cabbage, cut into serving pieces, and simmer for another half an hour. Add zucchini and cabbage and angel hair vermicelli. Simmer for 10 minutes more.

Serve in bowls with french bread and tossed green salad.

• • •

ROAST CHICKEN

Sprinkle the chicken with seasoning salt and paprika, then smear with soft butter. Place a whole peeled onion in the cavity, put in a hot oven, 400 F, and roast for 1 1/2 to 2 hours depending on size of the bird. Baste with juices in the pan every 20 minutes. For the first half of cooking time, lay a sheet of aluminum foil over the chicken to stop the breast from drying out.

Serve with roast potatoes and roast parsnips, and greens.

• • •

GRILLED CHICKEN, CORN, RED PEPPER & AVOCADO SALAD

A great lunch or dinner in the summer.

2 large avocados, peeled and diced
4 chicken breasts, boned but not skinned
6 ears of fresh corn (preferably yellow & white variety)

My Children of Light (1985 top, 1992 bottom)

2 peppers (anaheim or poblano) roasted, peeled,
seeded and diced
1 large red pepper, roasted, peeled, seeded and diced
1 head of red leaf lettuce, washed, dried and
torn into bite size pieces
Dressing:
2 tbsp. lime juice
2 tbsp. vinegar
1 cup olive oil
1/4 Maui onion or 2 green onions
1 bunch of cilantro (reserve some for garnish -1/4)
1 clove of garlic

Mix oil and vinegar, add oil slowly. Add cilantro to chop finely, add onion to chop medium fine. Set aside later salt and peppering to taste.

Corn:

Roast on charcoal or cook for 15 minutes in husk in microwave. Cool slightly, shuck and cut from cob.

Chicken:

Season with salt and pepper. Grill over charcoal or under broiler until brown. 8 minutes on skin side and 5 minutes on other. Cook at 275 F. Slice across grain and keep warm.

Place lettuce on a platter and toss together the corn, peppers, avocado and vinaigrette. Arrange the salad in the centre of the lettuce lined platter. Arrange chicken slices around salad and garnish with cilantro.

Makes 4 servings.

An easier version can be made substituting:

2 cups frozen corn, 1 9 oz can chopped chilies, 1 jar roasted red peppers.

• • •

GRILLED CHICKEN WITH ROSEMARY

Place cut up chicken in a broiler pan. Rub with butter and sprinkle with Lawry's seasoned salt. Put sprigs of rosemary all over chicken. Cover with foil, prick with a fork so some of the steam can escape. Put in the broiler and broil for 45 minutes. Then remove foil and cook for another 25-30 minutes. Turn once. The chicken should get nice and crispy.

• • •

ROLLED CHICKEN SUPREME

8 large chicken breasts
8 slices imported Swiss cheese
8 slices boiled ham
3 eggs
3 cups seasoned breadcrumbs
1 stick butter

Debone breasts. Prepare chicken by wrapping cheese and then ham around each breast. Secure well with wooden tooth-picks. Beat eggs; dip each piece of chicken in egg and roll in bread-crumbs. In a shallow baking dish, melt one stick of butter and add chicken. Place on low rack at 350 F and bake for 35 minutes, turning only once during cooking time. Baste often, adding more butter if necessary.

• • •

A GREAT CURRY SAUCE

Good party fare!
For chicken or seafood, from the heart of New Orleans.

2 onions, sliced
1 carrot, sliced
2 celery stalks, sliced
6 tablespoons of butter
6-8 tbsp. of curry powder
1 tsp. chili powder
6 tbsp. flour
2 cups of coconut milk*
salt to taste
1/4 tsp. mace
1/4 tsp. allspice
1/4 tsp. ground cloves
1/4 tsp. cinnamon
2 apples, chopped
4 tbsp. currant jelly
4 tbsp. chopped chutney
10 cups cooked chicken, cut into bite sized
pieces or 10 cups of cleaned boiled shrimp
*To make coconut milk, use one coconut per cup of regular milk.

Boil milk and put in blender with coconut meat and the liquid from the coconut. Puree and strain through cheese cloth.

Cook onion, carrot and celery in butter until soft. Add curry and chili powder and cook for 5 minutes. Blend in flour. Add coconut milk and stir until boiling. Add salt, mace, allspice, nutmeg, cloves, cinnamon and apple. Simmer for 1/2 hour and put through strainer. This much should be made a day ahead and allowed to set overnight. Put sauce in double boiler, heat and add chicken, or seafood stock. Serve with rice and side dishes of chopped eggs, bacon, green peppers, peanuts, pimentos, mashed bananas, pumpkin seeds, etc. Freezes well too!

• • •

FISH

We live near the ocean and fresh fish is always a treat. Maxwell doesn't cook very often but when he does, it's always delicious and presented very artistically. These are two of his favourite recipes.

MAXWELL'S RED SNAPPER

1 tsp. vanilla extract
4 tbsp. butter
5 tbsp. olive oil
1/4 cup finely chopped onion
1/2 cup crushed garlic
2 1/2 cups zucchini, cut in matchsticks
1 cup chopped tomatoes
2 tbsp. chopped basil (tsp. basil leaves)
1 tsp. crushed fennel seeds
3/4 tsp. salt
1/8 tsp. ground black pepper
1 1/2 lbs red snapper fillets

Sauce:
In a small saucepan mix 3 tbsp. butter, 2 tbsp. of olive oil with 1 tsp. of vanilla.

Zucchini:
Mix 1 tbsp. butter with 1 tbsp. oil, onion and garlic. Cook for 5 minutes. Add the zucchini and cook another minute.

Tomatoes:
Mix the tomatoes, fennel seeds, salt and pepper together in a saucepan and cook for 3 minutes.

Fish:

Take the fish fillets, add 2 tbsp. of olive oil. Cook over low heat. 2 minutes per side.

Serve the fish on a bed of zucchini and tomatoes. Garnish with lemon slices and add steamed baby carrots and snow peas.

• • •

MAXWELL'S TUNA CASSEROLE

Fabulous!

    5 oz pimento cheese
    12 oz can of cream of mushroom soup
    7 oz tuna
    7 oz cooked macaroni noodles
    1/2 cup of milk
    2 tbsp. butter
    1/2 cup of celery
    2 tbsp. of onion
    1/2 cup green olives
    1 cup crushed potato chips

Pre-heat the oven to 350 F. Mix all ingredients and place in a casserole baking dish. Sprinkle potato chips on top and bake for 15 minutes.

• • •

LADY MARY'S KEDGEREE

My Mother loves to serve this Kedgeree with saffron rice and a mixed green salad and toast.

2 cups of uncooked rice
2 lbs finnan haddie (or smoked haddock or salmon)
4 hard boiled eggs
1 stick of butter (4 oz), melted
2 tbsp. chopped watercress (or parsley)
1 cup raisins (plumped in brandy)
1 cup salted cashews
salt and freshly ground pepper to taste

Cook the rice until tender, but not mushy. Remove the skin and bones from the fish and flake. Chop the egg whites, sieve the egg yolks. Toss hot rice with melted butter. Add fish, raisins, nuts and toss lightly over the heat until piping hot. Garnish with chopped watercress and sieved eggs. Serve at once.

A more highly flavoured Kedgeree can be made by adding a teaspoon of curry powder or Worcestershire sauce and fresh lemon juice. Serves 4.

• • •

MOTHER'S SEAFOOD RAGOUT

This is a great dish to make for guests if you don't really feel like cooking. Use fresh shrimp and crabmeat if possible.

1 can of condensed cream of mushroom soup
1 cup evaporated milk
1/4 cup dry sherry or vermouth
1/8 tsp. thyme
1/8 tsp. basil
dash of pepper
1 10 oz pkt of frozen peas
1/2 lb shrimp, cleaned and cooked
1/2 lb sliced mushrooms

1/2 lb crabmeat, cooked
2 tsp. butter or margarine

Combine soup, milk, sherry, thyme, basil and pepper. Simmer over low heat, then add peas, shrimp and crabmeat. Saute mushrooms in butter and add seafood mixture. Serve over rice. Makes 5 servings.

• • •

FISH AND POTATO PIE

Poach 1 1/2 lb smoked haddock or cod fillet in 1/2 pint of milk. When cooked strain off and use to make 1/2 pint of white sauce. Flake fish, removing any skin and bones. Add the fish, 2 teaspoons of capers and seasoning to taste to the sauce. Place half the mixture in a greased oven-proof dish, add 2 sliced hard boiled eggs then cover with rest of the fish. Top with a layer of cooked potatoes (sliced) and sprinkle with cheese. Bake in a hot oven for 20-25 minutes. Makes 4 servings.

• • •

STUFFED TROUT

Melt 2 tablespoons of butter, add a squeeze of lemon juice, and 1/2 cup of chopped parsley. Then add 1/2 lb of fresh crabmeat. Heat through thoroughly. Toss boned trout in seasoned flour; stuff with buttered crabmeat. Saute trout in butter or bake in the oven with butter and a sprinkling of sherry.

• • •

SWORDFISH WITH ALMONDS

2 lbs Swordfish, almost 2" thick
1/2 cup of sweet butter
1/2 cup blanched, slivered almonds

Melt butter in skillet. When butter bubbles add fish and brown quickly on each side. Reduce heat and cook over low heat about 15 minutes on each side. This long, slow cooking violates all the rules - but just try it. Towards the last, add the almonds. With this swordfish I usually serve buttered Brussel sprouts or large lima beans and mashed potatoes.

• • •

ENGLISH FISH AND CHIPS

Sole, cod, snapper, orange roughy, bass - all fresh fish tastes delicious made this way. Dip in beaten egg then in breadcrumbs and fry in hot butter or olive oil. Fry for 4 or 5 minutes each side. Serve with french fries (chips) and eat out of yesterday's newspaper with your fingers!

• • •

And now for something sweet!
The Best of the Best

DESSERTS, CAKES, COOKIES AND PIES

While I was shooting the series Nanny and the Professor, there were many scenes in Nanny's kitchen. She was always preparing cups of tea and delicious things to eat, so I really got into cooking at that time. We all used to exchange recipes on the set, and to this day they are some of my best recipes. A lot of them, alas for the waistline, are cakes, cookies and pies! I was given this recipe for Carrot Cake by the key-grip (head carpenter), his name was Art. His wife used to put this delicious carrot cake in his lunch bag, and everyone would always be trying to cadge some off him. I thought it was one of the best cakes I've ever tasted. I still do. It's health food too. Except for the frosting!

CARROT CAKE

1 1/2 cups safflower oil
2 cups raw sugar
4 eggs - beat after each egg

Sift the following together and them mix the egg into the oil mixture.

2 cups unbleached white pastry flour - wholewheat
2 tsp. baking soda
2 tsp. baking powder
2 tsp. cinnamon
1 tsp. salt

Then add:

Cast from "Nanny and the Professor"

Juliet in "Nanny and the Professor"

3 cups shredded carrots
1 cup chopped walnuts

Pour into 2 square pans (9 x 9) and bake at 300 F for 50 minutes.

• • •

CARROT CAKE FROSTING

1 8 oz package of cream cheese
1 stick margarine, softened
4 tsp. vanilla
1 lb. powdered sugar

In a large bowl, mix together ingredients till smooth.

• • •

BASIC PIE CRUST

1 1/4 cups flour
1/4 tsp. salt
pinch of sugar
1 stick butter (chilled)
1/4 cup vegetable shortening
3-4 tbsp. water

Sift flour, salt and sugar into large mixing bowl. Cut butter and shortening into small pieces and cut into flour mixture rapidly. When shortening is the size of tiny peas, add water gradually, mixing lightly until dough holds together. Shape into a ball and refrigerate for 1/2 hour. Place on flour surface and roll out to 1/8" thickness, 2" larger than pie pan. Transfer to pan by rolling dough onto rolling pin and unroll into pan. Trim edges and flute.

• • •

VERMONT APPLE PIE

The maple syrup makes this special

    1/2 cup sugar
    1 tbsp. flour
    1/2 tsp. cinnamon
    1/8 tsp. salt
    3/4 cup ginger snap cookie crumbs, about 10-12
    5 tart apples, peeled and sliced
    1 unbaked 9" pie shell
    1/4 cup melted butter or margarine
    1/3 cup maple syrup
    whipped cream

Mix sugar, flour, cinnamon and salt. Stir in cookie crumbs. Place layer of apples in pie shell, top with layer of crumbs, then apples, then remaining crumbs. Pour melted butter evenly over top of pie. Bake at 400 F for 15 minutes. Reduce heat to 300 F and bake for 20 to 25 minutes longer. (If pie browns too fast, place a piece of foil lightly over the top.) Heat maple syrup up to boiling. Pour over pie and bake 15 minutes longer. Serve warm or cold with whipped cream.

• • •

KENTUCKY PECAN PIE

    1 cup white corn syrup
    1 cup dark brown sugar
    1/3 tsp. salt
    1/3 cup melted butter or margarine
    1 tsp. vanilla

3 whole eggs (slightly beaten)
1 heaping cup shelled whole pecans

Combine syrup, sugar, salt, butter, vanilla and mix well. Add slightly beaten eggs. Pour into a 9" unbaked pie shell. Sprinkle pecans over all. Bake in a preheated oven at 350 F for approximately 45 minutes. When cool, you may top with whipped cream or ice cream.

• • •

ENGLISH APPLE CRUMBLE

6 large apples, peeled and sliced
1/2 cup orange juice
1/2 cup granulated sugar
1/2 tsp. cinnamon
3/4 cup sifted flour
1/2 cup light brown sugar, packed
1/4 tsp. salt
6 tbsp. butter or margarine

Arrange apples in greased baking dish. Pour orange juice over apples. Combine granulated sugar and cinnamon, then sprinkle over apples. Combine flour, brown sugar, salt and butter with your fingers to make crumbly mixture. Spread over apples. Bake at 350 F until apples are tender and crust is lightly browned, about 45 minutes.

Variation: for nutty flavour, add 1/4 cup rolled oats and an additional tbsp. butter to the flour mixture for apple crisp. Makes 6 servings.

• • •

BLUEBERRY MUFFINS

Fabulous! Make these when blueberries are in season.

    2 cups all purpose flour
    1 cup sugar
    2 tsp. baking powder
    1/2 tsp. salt
    1/2 cup butter
    1/2 cup milk
    2 eggs
    1 tsp. vanilla extract
    2 1/2 cups blueberries
    sugar for sprinkling tops of muffins

Preheat oven to 375 F. Grease and flour a 12 cup muffin pan. In medium bowl combine dry ingredients. With pastry blender or two knives, cut in butter until mixture resembles coarse crumbs. In bowl combine milk, eggs and vanilla. Add to dry ingredients all at once, stirring just until moistened. Do not over-mix. Crush 1/2 cup of berries and add to batter. Fold in remaining berries and spoon into muffin pan. Sprinkle with sugar. Bake for 30 minutes or until toothpick inserted in centre comes out clean. Cool in pan for 5 minutes and turn onto wire rack. Makes 12.

• • •

RHUBARB PUDDING

    Pink spring rhubarb, as much as you please
    sugar to sweeten
    breadcrumbs to thicken

butter to enrich
lots of whipped cream

Cut rhubarb into 1" pieces. Arrange in buttered baking dish. Sprinkle generously with sugar. Then cover with breadcrumbs. Dot with butter. Spread alternate layers of sugared rhubarb and buttered crumbs until dish is 2/3 full. Bake at 375 F for about 40 minutes or until rhubarb is tender. Serve warm with very cold whipped cream.

• • •

CHEESECAKE - GRAHAM CRACKER CRUST

My family's favourite

1 lb cream cheese
3/4 cup caster sugar
2 eggs
juice of one lemon
1 tsp. vanilla

Cream the cream cheese, add sugar creaming until fluffy, add eggs, lemon juice and vanilla, beating thoroughly. Pour into Graham Cracker crust lined spring pan and bake for 35 minutes at 350 F. Take out of oven and pour this topping over it.

3/4 pint of sour cream
2 tsp. sugar
2 tsp. vanilla

Return to oven and bake for 5 minutes. Cool in spring pan.

Crust:

    10 Graham Crackers
    4 tbsp. butter
    2 tsp. sugar

Mix together and press into a greased spring pan.

• • •

PRUNE WHIP

    2 cups cooked prunes
    5 tbsp. sugar
    1/2 tsp. lemon extract
    1/2 cup shredded coconut
    1 cup dairy sour cream

Remove pits from prunes and chop fine. Add sugar and lemon extract and mix thoroughly. Stir in coconut, then add prune mixture in small amounts to sour cream, beating well. Chill before serving. Makes 6 servings.

• • •

APRICOT ALMOND FOOD

So simple and so delicious when apricots are in season.

    1 lb fresh apricots
    2 tbsp. granulated sugar
    1/2 pint cream (1/4 pint single and 1/4 pint double)
    1 tbsp. ground almonds

Stew apricots and sugar with a trace of water in saucepan or bake until the fruit is soft. When cool, rub through a sieve and combine the ground almonds with the puree. Whip the cream until it just holds a peak, and fold it into the fruit mixture. Spoon it into glasses, chill and serve with thin almond biscuits. This same mixture can be poured into the freezing tray to make a very good ice cream. Stir it once or twice during the freezing time to prevent ice crystals forming in it.

• • •

ENGLISH SUMMER PUDDING

I believe this was one of Queen Mary's favourites. It's beautiful to behold as well as delicious to eat.

Take the fruits of summer, especially dark berries, cut up into smallish pieces, add a little honey and water and cook gently for a few minutes. Take thin sliced white bread, cut off crusts and line a bowl with them. Pour in fruit mixture, then line top of bowl with bread until all is enclosed. (Keep some of the fruit and put in blender to liquify for the sauce).

Weight the fruit and bread mixture with a plate and something heavy to weight it down as much as possible. Put in the refrigerator for at least 4 hours or overnight. (You can take some of the sauce and spread it over the top of the pudding before you weight it down). Serve with sauce and whipped cream on the side.

• • •

ENGLISH TRIFLE

2 pkts of lady fingers
1 pkt frozen raspberries (fresh if available)
1 pkt frozen strawberries (fresh if available)
2 pkts Bird's Custard (an English secret to be found
in the gourmet section of the market)
2 pints milk
6 tbsp. sugar
sherry

Topping:
    1/2 pint of whipping cream
    1 tsp. sugar
    2 tsp. vanilla

Line glass bowl, bottom and sides with lady fingers. Sprinkle with sherry or kirsch, or fruit juices if it is for children. Heap in the fresh or frozen fruit. Make custard according to packet directions - pour over lady fingers and fruit. Cool. Whip cream, sugar and vanilla until it thickens, then heap onto trifle. Refrigerate for a few hours. Decorate with fresh fruit or grated chocolate and serve. A triumph! This serves 8 - 10.

• • •

BANANA BREAD

    1 3/4 cups flour
    2 tsp. baking powder
    1/2 tsp. salt
    1/4 tsp. baking soda
    1/3 cup shortening
    2/3 cup sugar
    2 eggs
    1 cup ripe, mashed bananas (2-3 bananas)

Sift together flour, baking powder, baking soda and salt. Beat shortening until creamy. Add sugar gradually and beat until light and fluffy. Add eggs and continue beating until well blended. Add flour mixture alternately with bananas, a small amount at a time, mixing after each addition only enough to moisten dry ingredients. Turn into greased loaf pan. Bake at 350 F for about 1 hour and 10 minutes or until done.

• • •

DATE-NUT BREAD

1/2 cup butter or margarine
1 cup sugar
1 egg

Mix well together, then add:

1 cup dates, chopped
1/2 cup walnuts, chopped
1/2 tsp. cinnamon
1/4 tsp. nutmeg
1/2 tsp. baking soda
1 cup boiling water
1 1/2 cups flour

Mix until fairly smooth. Pour into loaf pan. Bake at 350 F for 1 hour and 15 minutes. Allow to cool before removing from pan.

• • •

MOLASSES MEMORIES

Wonderful Xmas Cookies

3/4 cup shortening
1 cup sugar
1/4 cup molasses
1 egg
2 tsp. baking soda
2 cups flour
1/2 tsp. ground cloves
1/2 tsp. ground ginger

1 tsp. ground cinnamon

Melt shortening. Stir in sugar and molasses. Add egg, beating very well. Add baking soda, flour, cloves, ginger and cinnamon. Mix until well blended. Chill dough for a few minutes. Shape dough into size of small walnuts and roll in sugar. Place on greased baking sheet about 2" apart. Bake at 375 F for 10-12 minutes. Let stand for 2 minutes before removing them from baking sheet. Place on rack to cool. Makes 3 dozen cookies.

• • •

And believe it or not, a delicious avocado pie

ORPHA KLINKER'S AVOCADO PIE

Crust:
    1 cup flour
    1/2 cup soft butter
    1 cup chopped almonds
    1/4 cup brown sugar
Filling:
    2 egg yolks - beaten
    1 cup Eagle brand sweetened condensed milk
    1 large avocado, or two smaller ones, mashed
    1/2 cup lemon juice
    2 drops green food colouring (optional)
Topping:
    a cup whipping cream, whipped
    1 tbsp. sugar*
    1 tsp. vanilla*
    * added to cream

Preheat oven to 375 F. In 10" pan, press crust ingredients. into pan and bake until golden brown (approximately 10 minutes).

Chill. Mix filling ingredients together and pour into crust. Do not bake! Chill overnight.

Serve with whipped cream topping.

• • •

Maxwell and I have both been lucky enough to work with Jessica Tandy, a great lady and a great actress. I played her daughter in Five Finger Exercise when I was 17, and Maxwell did a play called Salonika with her at the Public Theatre in New York only a few years ago.

JESSICA'S BREAD & BUTTER PUDDING

6 slices stale white bread
softened melted butter
nutmeg
1/2 cup raisins (white soaked in sherry for 2 hours
-can use brandy or orange curacao)
3 eggs
1/2 cup sugar (for smaller recipe 1/4 cup)
salt
2 cups scalded milk
1 tsp. vanilla
blanched almonds (12-20)

Cut crusts off bread, cut into quarters and dip in melted butter to coat both sides. Arrange in a buttered baking dish. Sprinkle each layer with raisins and nutmeg (sparingly), finishing with bread on the top layer, sprinkle with nutmeg. Beat eggs, add sugar, scalded milk and vanilla. Strain over bread. Decorate top with blanched almonds. Put dish in a pan of hot water and bake in a 350 F oven for 45 minutes (add 3-5 minutes for crisper crust). Serve slightly warm.

• • •

Hayley and I in Noel Coward's "Fallen Angels" U.K. Tour. 1992

I am going to end this section with one of the most delicious desserts I have ever tasted - and I only discovered it recently. Hayley and I were on tour in the U.K. last year with a play called 'Fallen Angels', written by Noel Coward, who happens to be my Godfather, and I'm happy to say we had a great success and a lot of fun, touring England with Melissa, our dresser! While we were in Aberdeen, Scotland, we were introduced to "Sticky Toffee Pudding" at the Crown Hotel, Stonehaven. It is a famous pudding in Scotland, and so easy to make. Hayley and I pleaded for the recipe - and here it is.

STICKY TOFFEE PUDDING

6 oz pitted dates
1 tsp. bicarbonate of soda
1/2 pint of water
2 oz butter
6 grms castor sugar
2 eggs
6 oz self raising flour
1/2 lb butter
1 lb brown sugar
1 pt whipping cream

Simmer chopped dates, then add bicarbonate of soda. Cream butter and sugar, add beaten eggs, and fold in flour. Stir in date mixture. Put in a square pan and bake in oven at 350-400F for 20 to 25 minutes.

To make the sauce, melt butter, add sugar and cream and bring to a slow boil. Serve warm, spooned over pudding. Yum yum.

• • •

THE SOUL

"Psychic is of the Soul, the abilities to reason by the faculties, or by the mind, of the Soul ..."

Edgar Cayce

We are all psychic, and whether we choose to develop that potential power within us is purely a matter of choice. Unfortunately, spiritual education is not part of an ordinary school curriculum. We are taught to develop our mental ability and our physical ability, but there are no lessons in E.S.P., or mind reading, nor the ability to see the etheric body, or to read the aura colour which can give you a real insight about someone. It's not so much that you see the colour, as feel it. As a matter of fact, some very interesting work has been done in this field with blind children, they see aura colours! This is a true example of 'seeing with the third eye'. Aura reading is a great asset, it helps you to know what kind of a person you are dealing with. For example if someone is sick, or if they are lying, it shows up in their aura. Imagine how useful it would be in one's life, to be able to discern if someone wasn't telling the truth! Both in business and in personal relationships one would have a distinct advantage.

We are not taught to listen to that inner voice, that intuitive, all-knowing self, but most of us come to question the meaning of life, the meaning of death, and the word "coincidence" at some time or another. There is usually a catalyst that sets us off on the path of metaphysical inquiry; it can be a book we read, a conversation or an encounter we have; or an event in our lives that throws us into confusion; a period of time where we are forced into solitude; or if we are laid up in bed for a while through sickness.

"There is a reason for everything", and not only that, "Everything happens for the best". It's hard to always accept that, but very often looking back on some drama in your life, a really difficult, even tragic period, you can truly say something good came out of it; some step forward as far as your own personal growth and understanding is concerned. "Through the fire we are moulded..." And in those darkest times comes help, we are sustained, supported, so that we are able to come through it, enabling us to survive something in our lives, maybe we thought we never could. That support may come from people around us, but it also comes from our spiritual helpers, our guides, our guardian angels or whatever you wish to call them.

To me this is another very good reason to get into spiritual development, to start "tuning in", so to speak, to the wisdom and help that is there when we need it. I was watching the young girl Kimberly Beck, who contracted AIDS from her dentist, on television, and she was telling the story of her first days in the hospital after she'd been diagnosed with this terrifying disease. She said she was looking out of the window, crying and crying, full of fear and anger, and agonizing on why this should have happened to her. She closed her eyes, and as she lay there, she felt someone near her, on the bed, close to her, and she felt a great calm and peacefulness come over her, and she said she knew that everything was alright, whatever happened, it would be alright. She felt protected and not alone, there was a presence there with her conveying a message that truly comforted her, and gave her peace of mind that sustained her until the end.

When something extraordinary happens in your life, don't rush to rationalize it with your mind; look into it, expand your own realm of possibility, even experiment with it. I used to say "What a coincidence" quite often at one time, now I don't say it at all, the word is stricken from my vocabulary. If I am thinking about someone, family or friend, and within a few minutes the phone rings, or a letter arrives from that person, I don't believe it's a coincidence, it is telepathy, something the Masai in Kenya use on a day to day basis, and something that we in the West don't consciously use at all.

When I am away from home, far away in another country, in another time zone, and I think of my daughter Melissa, she will call me within minutes of my thinking of her. I've asked her "Why did you call me at this particular time?" And she'll say something like "I don't know Mummy, I just walked by the phone and picked it up without thinking."

Melissa is very psychic. She has running conversations with her imaginary friends, (spiritual guides), she believes in their loving protection and listens to their good advice. We all do that as children, but we have to relearn it as adults. Melissa also believes she has healing powers and practices E.S.P. This is largely due to the fact that I have shared with her a lot of the things I have learned over the last few years, and because she's so young she accepts magical concepts without mentally trying to justify them. She gives as good a reflexology treatment as I do, and is very good at "making people feel better". Also, Maxwell and I decided to send her to a Rudolph Steiner School from kindergarten through Grade IV where the focus is on the growth of the spiritual and creative nature of the child. There are over 100 of these schools in the U.S. and I cannot praise them too highly.

There were two catalysts in my life that awakened me out of my psychic sleep so to speak. The first was meeting and falling in love with Maxwell Caulfield, and the second was seeing Shirley Maclaine doing an interview on TV talking about her book "Out on a Limb", which at that point I had not read.

As anyone who has heard her speak knows, Shirley is brilliantly articulate on the subject of spirituality, and recounts her adventures courageously and honestly, shining a light for the rest of us should we be following along the path. The interviewer asked her, "What is your interpretation of the purpose of life?" Unhesitatingly Shirley answered "The purpose of life is to perfect the Soul until you are at one with God." It was if a light went on in my head, somehow I knew exactly what she meant, and I wanted to know more of what she knew. I went out immediately and bought "Out on a Limb", and reading it I found that many of the things she put so clearly into words, I already knew in my heart, in my innate self, but for some reason I had never investigated them.

Even when I did the TV series "Nanny and the Professor", which was about E.S.P., (extra sensory perception) and "magic", I just learnt the lines. I didn't explore the subject! I never questioned it and I totally believed in its authenticity, but obviously it just wasn't the right time for me.

Reading Shirley's book introduced me to Edgar Cayce, the renowned psychic. It's fascinating, once you are on the path of your own personal journey, and your eyes and ears are open, one thing inevitably leads to another; information seems to come at you from all sides, the next step always presents itself. My advice is "be open, read the signs, go with the flow; and if a book falls on your head in the library, read it!"

Once you start reading and delving into this subject of metaphysics, you can't stop, it's so interesting and there are so many wonderful books available.

Edgar Cayce is a good place to start, his biography "There Was A River" is extraordinary, as was the man himself. He was born in a small rural community in Kentucky and even as a child it was noticed he had strange and unusual "powers". Early in his life this was something of a cross to bear, but by the time he was 40 years old he had come to terms with it and was devoting his life to others. In the U.S. he is considered the father of holistic health. He would enter a self-induced trance, and working from no more than a sick person's name and address, (and they could be thousands of miles away) he would make a diagnosis of their condition and recommend effective treatments.

His readings, all 14,879 of them, are recorded and indexed in the library of the Association of Research and Enlightenment in Virginia Beach, Virginia. Anyone can become a member of the A.R.E. and have access to these readings, they will send them to you through the mail. Of course you can buy his books at any good bookstore.

The information that emanated from his unconscious mind covered subjects from pre-history to predicted earth changes. Most of his work, however, has to do with the human body, its nature, its diseases, and its healing capabilities.

"The spirit is the life, the mind is the builder, and the physical is the result."

Edgar Cayce

The Triune, The Balance, they all say the same thing in a different way; the spiritual teachers, the healers, the psychics, and it makes such perfect sense.

Cayce answered many questions on Karma, the Law of Cause and Effect. If you live your life by the Law, the Universal Law, and you know what you want, anything is possible. It is the Law taught by all the great religious leaders, Jesus, Krishna, Buddha. The Law is unchangeable:

"Whatsoever you sow, that must you reap"

and

"The manner in which you measure to others it will be measured to you again"

and

"Do unto others as you would have them do unto you"

One day purely as an exercise, go through the whole day applying the law of Karma. You will find it often changes your attitude or the way you speak to people, decisions you make. And it all comes back so fast, good Karma, or bad, you can turn your life around just thinking good thoughts for someone else, not being judgmental, and accepting people for what they are. Sometimes it almost seems as if the Karmic process has been speeded up, you get instant results. Perhaps the reason for that is we no longer have time for another lifetime of Karmic lessons; our beautiful planet,

Mother Earth, is sick, abused, stripped and poisoned, and we must do something about it fast. This is where we must concentrate our collective energy and new-found knowledge. We must speak out and do our part to turn the tide. It's not about waiting for governments and politicians to do something; we are the ones, we are part of the evolvement of the New Age, or as I prefer to call it the Age of Enlightenment. Each one of us is responsible, and if we begin to fulfill our potential as spiritual entities, and tap into the power source within, collectively we can change the course of the world. That is how important each and every one of us are.

In 1989, Robert Swan, the Englishman, with 8 other men from different countries, including one from the U.S., walked 500 miles in 57 days across the frozen sea to the North Pole. The seed was sown when he saw John Mills in 'Scot of the Antartic' 18 times as a boy. It was a brave and dangerous mission, they all got frostbite and some of them nearly lost their lives. On his return, Swan said he did it for two reasons; he wanted to see the hole in the ozone layer at the North Pole for himself, and he wanted to draw attention to the fact that each individual can do something, must do something about it. When asked what we can do, he said: "Plant a tree, every family go out and plant a tree. Don't use aerosol sprays. Recycle trash, and separate glass, plastics, tins and newspapers."

Now we can all do that.

"Awareness" is what it's all about. "Awareness" is why the celebrities are getting involved on such a grand scale, because through the media, they can reach so many.

When Jerry Garcia and the Grateful Dead did a benefit concert to save the Rainforests at Madison Square Garden, Jerry was quoted as saying "We've gotta do something about the Rainforest. They're burning it down, tearing it up even as we talk. 50 years it will all be gone. That's it. 50 years is not a long time anymore. That's in the lifespan of my kids. It's an alarming feeling. This is an earth problem - the whole earth. And who's left talking about it? Us. Why us? We're not qualified to do it, but we're going to do it, unless, or until, somebody else does."

Why us? I suppose the answer is because this is the Aquarian Age. The Age of Enlightenment, and we are the ones, and the time is now. And if we use all our resources, metaphysical and technological, we just may be able to turn things around.

Of course, giving money helps too and giving collectively would be very powerful. Imagine if everyone in the good ole U.S.A., man, woman and child sent $1 to an environmental group of their choice, on one special day! Earth Day for instance! What an impact it would have, both as to the amount of money sent, and the focus; the power of that collective visualization.

The destruction of the Rainforest and therefore the loss of more than 1 million species, a significant part of Earth's biological diversity and genetic heritage, and the breakdown of the ozone layer is much more of an immediate threat than nuclear war to humanity's continued existence.

Just for the fun of it, and for the sake of your good Karma, I have listed five environmental groups, all of them intent on arresting the wearing down and disintegration of our beautiful planet's precious resources, and delicate balance. They need you, and whatever you can afford is enough.

1. Greenpeace
    1436 V Street N.W.
    P.O. Box 3720
    Washington, D.C. 20007

2. Rainforests
    466 Green Street
    San Francisco, California 94133

3. World Wildlife Fund
    1250 Twenty-Fourth St. N.W.
    Washington, D.C. 20037

4. American Ocean's Campaign
    2219 Main Street, Suite 2B
    Santa Monica, California, 90405

5. The Wilderness Society
    1400 Eye Street N.W.
    Washington, D.C. 20005

6. William Holden Wildlife Foundation
    P.O. Box 67981
    Los Angeles, CA 90067

LOVE

"Love is the vibration which when expanded through cosmic attunement produces miracles"

As I said in the previous chapter there were two catalysts in my life that awakened me from my psychic slumber; the first was Maxwell. When perfect strangers meet and are instantly drawn together as familiar friends and passionate lovers, stirring deep feelings of recognition and love and loyalty, it is like being literally cat-

"Elephant Man", 1980

apulted into metaphysics. It made me seriously consider, for the first time, reincarnation and the past lives theory.

I met Maxwell in January 1980 on the 45th floor of the Minskoff building in New York City. We were rehearsing the play "Elephant Man"; he was playing the title role, John Merrick, and I was playing the actress Mrs. Kendall who befriends him. When I first saw Maxwell I was struck by a kind of luminous beauty about him, now I think I would recognize it as his "aura"; it was very bright; but I didn't know anything about that, then.

We were instantly drawn together, and became friends in that first 3 weeks of rehearsal. Firstly, I admired him tremendously, which is a good start in any relationship. He is an exceptionally talented actor, he had to be to have been cast in that leading role, he was very young and relatively unknown, except for the inner circles of New York theatregoers. He was appearing in an off-Broadway play call "Class Enemy" for which he won a Theatre World award. The man who had cast him, and me, therefore the one responsible for our meeting, was an immensely talented young Tony Award winning director named Jack Hofsiss. I remember thinking many times in the following weeks and months and years of happiness, how could we ever repay Jack for casting us together in that beautiful play. Well as it happens, we were able to repay him in a small way, and I shall come to that later.

It was as though I knew Maxwell, had always known him. I knew what he thought before he said it, I understood what he meant, I was completely relaxed with him, able to be myself, to be natural. My heart opened to him, I could tell him my innermost thoughts and secrets; I trusted him, and I loved him - unconditionally.

Unconditional love, both the giving and the receiving of it is a transforming experience. Because it is unselfish love, it opens up the heart chakra, and wakes you up psychically. It opens your eyes to the beauty of nature and quickens the pulse. The natural adrenalin of the body flows, and the spirit flows; you are more "tuned in" to the Universe, and more in touch with your Higher Self, that

We were married at Sunrise, December 2nd 1980.

Home on the ranch

inner voice that is all-knowing.

Luckily for me I heard only that voice; and the whispered warnings from well-meaning friends made not the slightest difference to what I knew in my heart. Here was my beloved, my soulmate, the man with whom I wanted to share the rest of my life.

We were married at sunrise on a clifftop overlooking the Pacific Ocean in December of that same year. He told me he would love me forever and I believed him. It was the most romantic day of my life, all planned to the minutest detail by Maxwell. He was 21 and I was 39, our birthdays are in November, one day apart.

Edgar Cayce poetically describes a soulmate as:
"The tongue to the groove, the tenon to the mortise."

It is more than just a physical attraction; it is a capacity to help one another at the physical, mental and spiritual levels.

Maxwell's great love for me, and mine for him, inspired me to explore my spiritual potential and the universal mind. He has been so supportive of all my endeavours, and his regard for me lifted my own self-esteem, helping me to believe anything is possible, and that if you can dream it, you can do it. He put me in touch with the essence of me, and helped me along the path of discovery, toward my understanding of the meaning of life.

I remember when I first took Maxwell to meet my parents at their beautiful 17th century house 40 miles from London. He was helping my Mother carry some logs in from the garden; and as she knelt by the fire looking up at him, I heard her say, "I know you; we're old friends".

She knew him too, from long ago and faraway.

Someone asked me the other day; "What proof do you have of reincarnation?" Of course I don't have any proof; anyway what is proof to me wouldn't be proof to anyone else; and it's not something I know in my head, it's something I feel in my heart. Everyone finds their own answers and their own understanding in their own time.

I love living in the land of the American Indian, they were such a highly evolved race, so close to God through nature, and very much in tune with the universe, the incredibly beautiful Mother Earth, as yet untouched by human hand or civilisation.

Staring out over the Grand Canyon in Arizona, the magnificence and beauty is staggering; it is as though you can hear God breathing. I believe anyone who goes there is replenished spiritually, in some way.

Nature heals; that's why people who go hiking, into the mountains or deserts, return home physically and spiritually revived, healed by nature; by living, growing plants and flowers; by beautiful birds and animals; crimson sunsets and silver dawns, and the stars and the moon and the midnight sky. Nature heals and replenishes us all the time if we allow it to. It is so easy to get locked into our world of bricks and mortar, our concrete jungles. One of the great inspirations known to man is the dark night sky full of stars, nowadays many people living in the big towns and cities never see a dark sky full of stars; "The Dome of Heaven", as my Mother calls it.

HEALING

"A healer is one with the abilities to arouse within its fellow man, the consciousness, that is the tone and all healing influence in a physical body."

Edgar Cayce

We are all healers, we can heal ourselves and we can heal each other. Unfortunately, over the last couple of decades especially, we have come to rely too much on doctors to make us well instantly; we want pills or medicines for "immediate relief".

Sometimes, mostly in fact, the body needs to "go through that sickness", the sickness needs to "run its course" because that is the way the body is ridding itself of toxic buildup, or revealing that something we are doing is not agreeable to it. Very often disease of the physical body is caused by un-ease of the mental body; i.e. stress.

Then also it can be a gradual physical breakdown because we are not eating right; not feeding the cells and the blood, the muscle, the nerves and the bones; not receiving the vitamins and minerals through the food we eat, that the body needs to function at its optimum level. It will keep going a long time, abused and neglected, but eventually it will break down, then you have to build it up again, patiently and persistently.

Homeopathic remedies are not as instant as drug remedies at alleviating the symptoms or the pain of disease. But with homeopathic cures you know when the symptoms and the pain disappear, the cause of the problem has been corrected, not just subdued or anaesthetized.

Physically we are a brilliant and scientifically mysterious organism. You hear doctors and scientists say "We don't know what causes it," or when they talk about a deadly virus or a terminal disease "we don't know what is the exact purpose of the pituitary gland, or how it works but ..."

We can send men into space and bring them back, but the miracle of the body is still to a great degree unfathomable. Millions and millions of dollars are spent in research every year on different drugs; they experiment with them on animals and people, with no idea what the side effects are going to be, until they show up on the "guinea pig"; sometimes years later.

They are experimenting, so let us experiment too, in a different way. In the privacy of our own homes, with our new-found but ancient knowledge, and the confidence in our ability to "tune into the Triune of our inner beings", to find out what's wrong, and do something about it.

Next time you're not feeling well, stop for a minute, sit down quietly and meditate on the state of your health. What do you feel in your heart your body needs? What do you know in your heart you are doing wrong? Maybe there's something you've been ignoring, allowing it to get worse; a sore back, a headache, a pain in your chest or your stomach, a little cough that won't go away. Be honest and open with yourself; take a few deep breaths and don't be afraid.

For the past few years my healing Bible has been a wonderful little paperback called "The Edgar Cayce Remedies", by William McGarey M.D., a healing doctor who has devoted a life study to Cayce's concepts of body function, and combines it with his scientific knowledge, to heal the sick. I have given numerous copies of this book to friends, it is the best introduction to Cayce's healing remedies. In Dr. McGarey's words:

"Illness it seems to me, often is like a pitfall into which one stumbles in the darkness of night. For the illness actually does come from our lack of awareness of where our activities or emotions and attitudes are taking us, or sometimes we simply don't care.

So it is important to assess our own attitudes. See if they are contributing to our illnesses. Better yet appraise deep within our own selves what attitudes we want to develop that are both constructive and that build health and a vigorous body balance. Then we need to act, for action makes it real, and in this way our healing progresses."

So start off by getting your attitude working constructively for you, and then go to work on the practical things you can do for yourself. If you've got a little cold, or flu coming on, you need a good shot of Vitamin C, so go and buy a bag of oranges and drink the juice all day, freshly squeezed juice if possible and visualise the vitamins and the iron and the calcium of that sunshine-filled fruit permeating your system. Or take a heavy dosage of Vitamin C tablets for a few days and cut out sugar. But do something - don't just wait for the cold to come doing all the wrong things.

Maybe it is time to rethink your diet; fast for a day or two; start taking a daily walk; practice deep slow breathing drawing in the 'pranha', or life force, and recharging yourself with the cosmic power of the Universe. Focus on your health rather than on your sickness. Visualize the healing process, consciously direct the body cells.

Cayce says: "Each atom in a body that becomes cut off by disease, distrust, or injury, needs to be awakened to its necessity of co-ordination with other portions of the body."

It's a very good idea to go to a chiropractor for a check-up and to make sure you are aligned, with nothing blocking the energy flow; no vertebrae out of place, no muscle constricted or knotted. The spinal column is the lifeline of the nervous system, and deserves the best of care and maintenance. An occasional visit to a chiropractor ensures that your body is operating at its full potential and therefore is capable of maintaining perfect health.

Misalignments can create pressure on nerve tissue and thus interfere with the conduction of nerve impulses to other parts of the body. It is a misconception that you only go to a chiropractor when you've got "a bad back".

In many of his readings, Edgar Cayce advised chiropractic and massage. He said:

"It is not merely the punching in of a certain segment or the cracking of bones, but it is a keeping of BALANCE, by the touch, between the sympathetic and the cerebrospinal system."

and

"There is no form of physical mechanotherapy so near in accord with NATURE'S measures as correctly given osteopathic adjustments."

By all means go to a doctor for some good advice as well, but make sure the doctor you go to is a vocational healing doctor interested in preventative medicine, and not just the disbursement of the latest drugs, and big bills.

The biological fact is if we nourish the body, and feed it properly, it can renew itself. It can build new cells that are worn out or sick. And we can use visualization to direct the healing forces wherever they are needed. Imagine there are billions of cells in the body, each with its own aura of consciousness, and imagine that you are activating that consciousness toward your healing potential.

A few years ago I took some psychic development classes in New York. Jason, our teacher asked us to choose two methods for developing psychic ability; one could choose from Astrology, Clairvoyance, Clairaudience, Tarot, Numerology, Healing, Psychometry etc. I chose Healing and Tarot.

I didn't know what sort of healing I wanted to practice but I knew it would be some sort of laying on of hands. All healing, all force, all power comes from the Infinite; and I wanted to learn how to be an instrument of that healing power. Shortly after that class, Reflexology just presented itself to me.

I was walking along the street in New York, and I saw an advertisement for a weekend seminar on Reflexology given by Laura Norman. Laura is a pioneer in spreading the word of this ancient healing art in the U.S., and has recently published a wonderfully informative book on the subject called "Feet First". (The chart on the following pages is reproduced from that book.) I found her course fascinating, familiar, and entirely logical.

Maybe it all made such sense to me because I have always loved having my own feet massaged; or maybe because I used to massage my Father's feet when I was a little girl. He said it made him feel wonderful. Hayley and I, 5 and 9 respectively, had a "pretend beauty salon" at home, and Daddy was our one and only customer. He would stay in the chair for hours having manicures, and pedicures, and massages, and hairdos! All the while regaling us with wonderful stories and conversation, anything to keep us going. One of my 'treatments' was a "footrub". Maybe it was past life recall that made Reflexology seem so familiar to me; perhaps I practised it in Egypt many moons ago, anyway it has become my healing method, and a way for me to make someone feel better.

The first records of reflexology were hieroglyphics found on an Egyptian tomb, a physician's tomb, circa 2300 B.C. The scientific facts are that there are reflex points in the feet that correspond to every organ and gland in the body. There are 7200 nerve endings in each foot; and with massage and gentle pressure, you can relax muscles, release tension, reduce stress, and breakdown calcium deposits, which are absorbed into the blood stream and eliminated. It cleanses the body of toxins and impurities. A healthy body is like a healthy home, you have to take out the garbage regularly. By deepening relaxation, reflexology causes all the systems of the body to function more efficiently, including those that eliminate waste products.

In the words of my father's 90 year old homeopathic doctor: "The root of all disease is deficient drainage!"

Reflexology will improve nerve function and circulation, and relieve aching in the neck, shoulders, lower back, and of course, in the feet themselves.

Very often when friends came to see us I will give them a reflexology treatment and after a long weekend of cooking and entertaining and being on my feet, Maxwell or Melissa will give me one. It takes all the aches away and it's much better than a sleeping

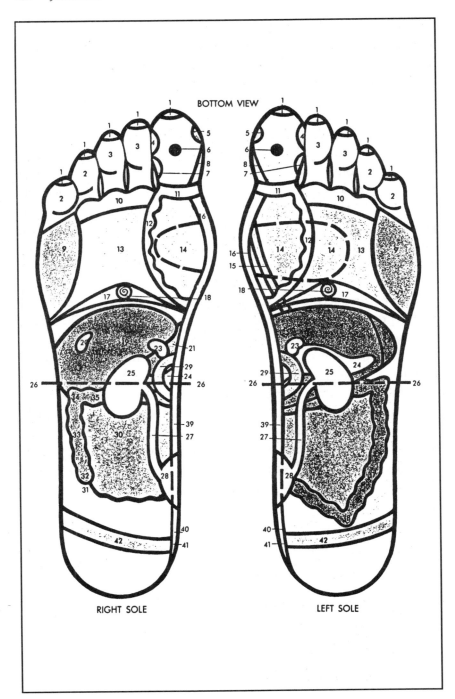

pill, for instead of waking up groggy or depressed, you wake up light as a feather. It's one of those wonderful sciences that you can learn, and practice at home, on yourself and on your family. Children love it, it puts them right to sleep.

LAURA NORMAN'S FOOT REFLEXOLOGY CHARTS

1. BRAIN
2. SINUSES/OUTER EAR
3. SINUSES/INNER EAR
4. TEMPLE
5. PINEAL/HYPOTHALAMUS
6. PITUITARY
7. SIDE OF NECK
8. CERVICAL SPINE (C1-C7)
9. SHOULDER/ARM
10. NECK/HELPER TO EYE, INNER EAR, EUSTACHIAN TUBE
11. NECK/THYROID/PARATHYROID/TONSILS
12. BRONCHIAL/THYROID HELPER
13. CHEST/LUNG
14. HEART
15. ESOPHAGUS
16. THORACIC SPINE (T1-T12)
17. DIAPHRAGM
18. SOLAR PLEXUS
19. LIVER
20. GALLBLADDER
21. STOMACH
22. SPLEEN
23. ADRENALS
24. PANCREAS
25. KIDNEY
26. WAIST LINE
27. URETER TUBE
28. BLADDER
29. DUODENUM
30. SMALL INTESTINE
31. APPENDIX
32. ILEOCECAL VALVE
33. ASCENDING COLON
34. HEPATIC FLEXURE
35. TRANSVERSE COLON
36. SPLENIC FLEXURE
37. DESCENDING COLON
38. SIGMOID COLON

39.   LUMBAR SPINE (L1-L5)
40.   SACRAL SPINE
41.   COCCYX
42.   SCIATIC NERVE

"Early man roved over plains, through forests, and stepped on sharp objects which pressed into his feet, reaching the tiny electrical reflexes, furnishing a natural massage... The electrical shock stimulated the portion of the body for which that part of the foot was responsible, and the body as a whole was in rhythm with the Universe."

> Mildred Carter
> Helping yourself
> with Reflexology

My interest in the healing arts and sciences extended into other areas; I studied aromatherapy, iridology, crystal and colour healing, I even made my own flower essences, I read up on American Indian healing rituals and herbal remedies. About the same time I discovered that the ranch we had just bought in Santa Barbara was on land that used to belong to the Chumash Indians who were also known as the "Rainbow People", famous for their colour healing therapies!

One day during this period, Maxwell and I received a shocking phone call telling us that our friend and mentor, Jack Hofsiss, the director who had cast us together in the 'Elephant Man', had had a terrible accident. He had dived into the shallow end of a swimming pool on Fire Island in New York, and had hit the bottom and broken his neck. On top of that the tragedy was that no one nearby realised what had happened and he was under the water a long time. By the time they got him out and flew him in a helicopter to New York City, he was in a very bad way. He couldn't use his arms or his legs, he was paralysed from the neck down.

He spent 8 long months at the Rusk Institute in New York, where he recovered some use of one arm, but he was suffering terribly mentally and emotionally. Most of the time he wished he had died at the bottom of that pool. Also physically he was very debilitated after 8 months of hospital food; he says all he remembers is white bread and lime jello! I must say it always amazes me that these facilities where sick people are 'in recovery', pay so little attention to nutritional eating.

When Jack was finally getting out of the hospital, we heard he was going to stay with a friend in Santa Monica, California. I decided if I could get my hands on him, so to speak, I could help him. I was convinced of it. So we invited him, and he accepted the invitation, and the challenge. Maxwell and I rented a beautiful little house for him way up in the mountains of Santa Barbara. We furnished it very simply, rented a hospital bed and built ramps from one level to another for the wheelchair, he was going to be there for a month. He was accompanied by a marvellous woman, a nurse he had met at the hospital, called Maureen. She embraced all my theories and was very excited at the prospect of a month of "healing."

When he arrived he was terribly depressed, he didn't really want to live, he couldn't sleep at night, he had a recurring kidney infection, and almost worst of all, for him, he couldn't read for more than about 10 minutes at a time, because his eyes would lose focus.

Well, I threw the book at him, as it were; I started him on an intensive programme which I had carefully planned, of fasting, reflexology, meditation, visualization, epsom salt baths, and sunbaths, colonic irrigation and massage, castor oil packs, healing with colour and light and music and drinking pints of solarized water!

In 10 days, after 4 days of fasting, followed by a strict diet of fresh fruit and vegetables, brown bread, brown rice, pasta and a little fish and chicken, plus fresh air and sunshine and all of the previously mentioned treatments, there was a marked improvement. He was sleeping as much as 12 to 14 hours a night; and his eyesight was so improved he was able to read for 3 to 4 hours at a time; his kidney infection disappeared and he was taking no medication, his skin colour was better, and almost best of all his attitude and his state of mind had improved. He was suddenly happy to be alive after all, and making plans to go back to work, directing in New York.

And with determined effort from him, and massage and physiotherapy from Maureen and I, he began to get movement and control in both his hands and arms, so that he could be a little more independent.

When he and Maureen left the little house in the mountains a month later, he was a different person from the one who had arrived. He was full of life and humour and plans for the future, and Maxwell and I felt we had in some way been able to repay him for the wonderful gift he had given us - each other.

It seemed a small miracle and Jack was so grateful; and really all I had done was put him in touch with his own consciousness, his own powers; the powers that are the true and healing influences in a physical body.

KRIYA YOGA

"Through the use of the "Kriya Key" persons who cannot bring themselves to believe in the divinity of any man will behold at last the full divinity of their own selves."

Paramahansa Yogananda
Autobiography of a Yogi

I realise now I rejected organised religion when I was quite young, I was still at school actually; maybe it had something to do with the rogueish chaplain at our school who used to 'ping' girl's bra straps in the vestry before the Sunday service. I was in the choir and very disapproving.

I always believed in God, but once I left home I didn't feel the need to go to Church to feel close to Him. Sometimes it's nice to go to Church and sing and pray and hear a good sermon, but it is much more important to walk with God in your heart and to live your life everyday as if you are God. I never like the hell and damnation preached from the pulpit, preying on people's fear and guilt. The Old Testament is ostensibly a Book of War, as is the Iliad; the Bhagavad Gita too is part of one of the great war epics of all time.

God is everywhere, in everything, but is easier to recognise in someone like Mother Teresa or Florence Nightingale, or a doctor working selflessly in a refugee camp alleviating the suffering of others, than in ourselves. God is in a sunset, or a sunrise, or a great storm over the ocean; or in an egg, or a rose, or a cat's whisker; and inside each of us - there is God. Jesus and Krishna and Buddha were highly evolved Souls, they were God incarnate, and their teachings, though different, were the same. In a sense we are all God incarnate. I believe we return time and time again to this earthly life in order to perfect the Soul; to be at one with God; to make sure that little spark of God that lies within each and every one of us is burning brightly.

I had read about Kriya Yoga years ago, the secret key of Kriya as it is referred to in the "Autobiography of a Yogi". It is mentioned in several of my yoga books, but none of them ever explained exactly what it was or how to do it. But as the saying goes, "When the student is ready, the teacher will appear", so at the beginning of last year when friends told me that an Indian Master was going to be in California giving lectures, and that he taught the Kriya, I knew I must go and see him.

Maxwell and I went to Carmel where he was giving a two day course called "The Art of Living". His name is Pundit Ravi Shankar, affectionately know as Punditiji, he is a spiritual teacher, a man considered to be a living saint by tens of thousands of people in India.

When he walked into the hall, where we sat waiting, in his long white robes, his dark hair flowing around his shoulders, and he smiled at us, his face and his eyes were so full of love and joy, I felt my heart immediately open to him. I knew that here is a man who is in touch with the Godliness inside himself, and it literally shines out of him. He is on a higher level of consciousness, a higher vibrational level than the average person; and being in his presence lifts you onto a higher vibration also.

Punditiji travels all over the world teaching the Sudharshan Kriya. Sudharshan means "the right vision of who I am", and it is a powerful meditation technique in which, through the breath, you release all the anger and frustration and tension from every cell of your body; every cell of your body is energized and oxygenized.

You know when you get angry or unhappy you don't just feel it in your stomach or your head, it gets stored in every cell.

The Kriya completely clears and releases all the stresses, in just a few days. With deep breathing this yoga oxygenates the blood and the cells, and has a most wonderful cleansing and healing effect on the whole system.

90% of the impurities in the body are eliminated through the breath, and we use only 30% of our lung capacity. Practising Kriya you increase the use of your lung capacity, and increase your ability to release anger and fear and stress which are the primary cause of disease in the physical and mental body.

Doing Kriya for the first time, people have various reactions; some people laugh or cry uncontrollably for a few minutes; sometimes parts of the body get numb, some people get cramps or see visions, but afterwards, and one can do it for as long as 15 minutes to one hour, one feels very light and very peaceful, you feel the benefit instantly. There has been a cleansing, and a purifying of the whole system.

The mind, the body and the Soul feel very balanced and therefore you feel very happy. Punditiji says "it lifts old Karma", and we all have some of that stored away somewhere!

Kriya is not something you can learn from a book or a tape, you have to be taught by someone qualified. Of course to be taught by a Master like Punditiji is the optimum best; let us not underestimate "the grace of the Guru;" but Punditiji has taught others all over the world to teach this form of yoga, and there are already centres in several major cities across the U.S. and Canada, where there are qualified teachers. You can find out if there is someone in your area by contacting:

The Art of Living Foundation
P.O. Box 50003
Montecito, California, 93108

Once you've taken a course you can practice at home, and use it as a spiritual tool to help you attain that state of inner joy to which we all aspire, consciously or unconsciously. With the Kriya one is able to keep that peace, to be in a state of love - unconditional love, at one with yourself and at one with God. So when emotional upheavals come, they come and they leave you, they don't stay, they come and they go. They don't permeate the cells and unbalance the system.

This method combined with good food and good rest and proper mental attitude is a powerful healing force. There are many instances of people with serious disease being cured, by practising the Kriya.

I hope that this has been interesting and informative reading for you, my reader, maybe even enlightening in some way.

Everyday we wake up with choices, and not to listen to that inner voice, not to try to tap into that power source within us is, I think, wasting valuable time; and time is of the essence, both for our own fulfilment, and for the healing of our planet, so that it may continue to sustain our children, and our children's children.

If we ourselves are in balance, in harmony, and in health, and we can find and use our own individual power to better our lives, and the lives of those around us, and therefore the planet itself; then we will truly be a part of the healing of the Universe. And that is pretty important.

PRAYER

"Meditating is listening to God, Prayer is talking to God."

Edgar Cayce

Prayer is a spiritual tool that we often forget to use in an everyday sense. You don't have to be in Church to pray, nor does your life have to be in jeopardy before you call out to God for help. You can pray anywhere, at any time; standing up, lying down or on your knees.

Many people have turned away from organized religion and stopped going to church; scripture is no longer a required class in school, and mothers don't teach their children to say their prayers at night, as our mothers taught us, therefore giving the security of knowing that there is a God in heaven who loves us all. Religious wars ravage countries like the former Yugoslavia, creating untold grief and suffering. All the more reason to pray, to pray unceasingly; to pray for ourselves and each other; to pray collectively or separately for guidance and forgiveness; to pray for those who do not believe, who do not feel love for God and their fellow man in their hearts.

Your prayers may be the rosary said slowly with diligence and devotion to keep your mind on the love of God. Or it may be chanting with the Japa beads, praising God in Krishna consciousness; or intoning in the Jewish temple. Or it may be the stilling of the mind in an hour of devoted meditation. But whatever prayer you know, whatever call or prayer reaches your heart most deeply, pray that love may grow and fulfill itself through you, through your mind's thanksgiving and humbleness, in realization that every good and perfect gift: grace, love, peace and discernment really comes from love itself -- God.

Jesus said: "Ask and ye shall know, Seek and ye shall find." It is vital that we have a personal dialogue with God, that we ask for guidance and protection from Him, for ourselves and our loved ones.

Flood your mind with violet light, breathe in the pranha of life, and take up the responsibility that is on us to heal the planet, starting with the balancing of our own lives, and the lives of those around us. We, the women of the world, are the nurturers of the family; we put the food on the table that will nourish the physical bodies of our loved ones; we are the teachers of our children from babyhood, and we must teach them about love and God and the Law of Karma. Harmony at home will lead to harmony outside of the home. If the body is healthy and in balance with the mind; if we nurture the soul with meditation and prayer, we will be doing our part to heal the world, and that is pretty important.

> "Your life is like a burning candle.
> You are burning every minute, every second.
> And if you are aware of the burning of your life,
> That becomes a prayer.
> Regardless, it is happening."

> --Sri Sri Pundit Ravi Shankar

Pundit Ravi Shankar "Punditiji"

MY PRAYER

God bless Mummy and Daddy, Hayley and Jonathan, Mark and Shirley, all my Aunties and Uncles and Nephews, all my friends and relations and everyone who I love. And please great Father of the mountains and rivers, throw your light and protection around my beloved husband Maxwell, and my beautiful children Sean and Melissa and my granddaughter Cheyanne, make them wise and keep them safe. And make me a channel through which your love shines.

Amen.